KS2
Success

PRACTICE TEST PAPERS

Maths, English
and Science

**Jason White, Jon Goulding, Rachel Axten-Higgs,
Jackie Clegg and Bob McDuell**

Contents

Contents

Science

Answers and Mark Scheme

Acknowledgments

Cover and P1 ©2003-2011 Shutterstock Images LLC, © Hemera/Thinkstock; P100/101 ©iStockphoto/Thinkstock; P102/103 Extract from E. Nesbit's *The Railway Children*; ©Zoonar/Thinkstock; P104 ©iStockphoto/Thinkstock; P107 Interview with the Railway Children, with thanks to Pete Coleman of www.the-railway-children.co.uk; P109 ©Hemera/Thinkstock; P124 ©Jupiterimages/liquidlibrary/Thinkstock, ©iStockphoto/Thinkstock; P125 ©iStockphoto/Thinkstock; P126 ©Ingram Publishing/Thinkstock; P127 ©iStockphoto/Thinkstock; P128 Image of Helen Thayer © Helen Thayer; P129: Extract *Roald Amundsen*, from 100 Greatest Men, 1995, Anova Books; P132: EXPLORER ©Alan Brownjohn 1969, 1997. Alan Brownjohn's poem EXPLORER reproduced by kind permission of the author c/o Rosica Colin Limited, London; P240 © iStockphoto/Thinkstock

Introduction

How these Tests will Help your Child

These practice test papers can be used at any time throughout the year to provide practice for the Key Stage 2 tests. The papers will provide a good idea of the strengths and weaknesses of your child.

The answers and mark scheme have been provided to enable you to check how your child has performed.

When an area of weakness has been identified, it is useful to go over these, and similar types of questions, with your child. Sometimes your child will be familiar with the subject matter but might not understand what the question is asking. This will become apparent when talking to your child.

Administering the Tests

- Provide your child with a quiet environment where they can complete their test undisturbed.
- Provide your child with the following equipment (as required): pencil, ruler, rubber, calculator, protractor, etc.
- The amount of time given for each test varies, so always consult the front page of each paper.
- You should only read the instructions out to your child.

The instructions for how to administer the Mental Arithmetic papers and the Spelling papers for the Grammar, Punctuation and Spelling test have been included in the answer section. This will enable you to administer these elements of the test to your child.

Marking the Tests and Assessing Levels

Make sure your child has completed all the relevant papers for each set. Mark the practice test papers using the answers and mark scheme provided at the back of the book. It is useful to share the marking with your child as this will help to familiarise them with how best to approach each format of test question.

At the end of Key Stage 2, most students are expected to achieve Level 4 and some students will reach Level 5. However, for some children, achieving Level 3 is a real success for that individual. A child achieving Level 5 is working to a high level and, in exceptional cases, a child may reach Level 6.

Please note: these tests are **only a guide** to the level or mark that your child can achieve and cannot guarantee the same level is achieved during their Key Stage 2 tests. The levels given on pages 5–6 are only intended for general guidance as the threshold of the levels changes from year to year.

Maths

Add up the marks for each paper and write them in the corresponding tables below. Once you have a total mark out of 100, look at the table below to find out what National Curriculum level it matches to.

Levels 3–5	Set A	Set B	Set C
Test Paper 1 (out of 40)			
Test Paper 2 (out of 40)			
Mental Arithmetic (out of 20)			
Total (out of 100)			

Level	Mark range (total / 100)
2	15–20
3	21–50
4	51–80
5	81–100

English (Reading)

Add up the marks for each paper and write them in the corresponding tables below. Once you have your total mark out of 50, look at the table below to find out what National Curriculum level it matches to.

Levels 3–5	Set A	Set B
Reading test (out of 50)		

Level	Mark range (total / 50)
Below Level 3	Up to 10
3	11–22
4	23–35
5	36–50

Please note: for the English test, the marks for the Reading paper will be combined with the marks for the Writing Paper (teacher assessed) to produce a combined English score.

Grammar, Punctuation and Spelling

Add up the marks for each paper and write them in the corresponding tables below.

Levels 3–5	Set A	Set B	Set C
Paper 1: short answer questions			
Paper 2: spelling			

Level 6	Set A
Paper 1: extended task	
Paper 2: short answer questions	
Paper 3: spelling	

Please note: level ranges have not been provided for the Grammar, Punctuation and Spelling papers because, at the time of writing, they were unknown.

Science

Add up the marks for each paper and write them in the corresponding tables below.

Once you have your total mark out of 80, look at the table below to find out what National Curriculum level it matches to.

Levels 3–5	Set A	Set B	Set C
Test Paper 1 (out of 40)			
Test Paper 2 (out of 40)			
Total (out of 80)			

Level	Mark range (total / 80)
Below Level 3	0–17
3	18–40
4	41–60
5	61–80

Test Paper 1 (calculator **not** allowed)

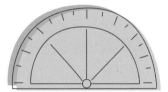

Instructions:

- find a quiet place where you can sit down and complete the test paper undisturbed
- make sure you have all the necessary equipment to complete the test paper
- read the questions carefully
- answer all the questions in this test paper
- go through and check your answers when you have finished the test paper

Time:

This test paper is **45 minutes** long.

Note to Parents:

Check how your child has done against the Answers and Mark Scheme on pages 287–288.

Page	9	11	13	15	17	19	20	Max. Mark	**Actual Mark**
Score	....	....	....	....	....	....	....	40	....

First name   Jenna

Last name   George

1 Write the missing numbers in the calculations below.

a) $6.3 \times \boxed{} = 6300$

(1 mark)

b) $1040 \div 100 = \boxed{1^{r40}}$

(1 mark)

2 Here is a square divided into identical smaller squares.

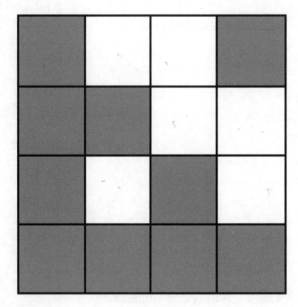

What fraction of the square is **not** shaded?

(1 mark)

3 The toy shop has a sale on: *Buy one and get one free.*

Train Set £1.99

Doll £2.99

Car £1.55

Kate has £10 to spend.

a) What is the greatest number
of dolls she can buy with her money? `2` *(1 mark)*

Q3a

b) How much money will she
have left if she wants **only 2** dolls? £ `2.99` *(1 mark)*

Q3b

4 Write the next two numbers in the sequence.

15   45   75   105   `135`   `165`   *(1 mark)*

Q4

subtotal

5 This is the time Sally starts her walk to grandma's house.

The walk takes 45 minutes.

What time did Sally arrive at grandma's?

$\boxed{11:42}$

(1 mark)

6 Round these decimals to the nearest whole number.

27.6 m $\boxed{30.0}$ m   79.4 km $\boxed{80.0}$ km

(1 mark)

7 Ben did a survey in school about the children's pets.

He then drew this Venn diagram.

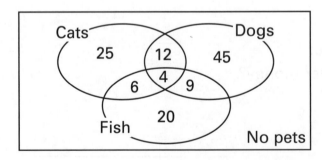

a) **How many children had a dog for a pet?** $\boxed{70}$ *(1 mark)*

b) **Which was the least popular pet?**

Circle the correct answer.   CAT   DOG   (FISH)   *(1 mark)*

8 Measure accurately the **longest side** of this shape.

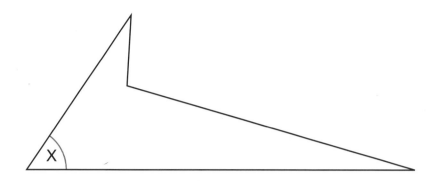

a) Give your answer in millimetres. | 10.17 | ~~CM~~ mm | *(1 mark)*

b) Measure the **angle x** using a protractor. | 55 |° *(1 mark)*

9 Circle **two** numbers that add up to make **0.81**

(0.24)   0.09   0.9   0.51   (0.57)   0.17   *(1 mark)*

10 Sam weighs some sand. He weighs 225 grams of sand.

Draw an arrow on the scale to show 225 grams. *(1 mark)*

subtotal

11 Circle **two** different numbers which multiply together to make 1 million.

50   200   5000   20 000   100 000   *(1 mark)*

12 Circle **all** the multiples of 9 in the list of numbers.

19   29   (36)   51   (81)   *(1 mark)*

13 Complete the diagram below to make a shape that is symmetrical about the mirror line.

Use a ruler. You may also use a mirror or tracing paper.

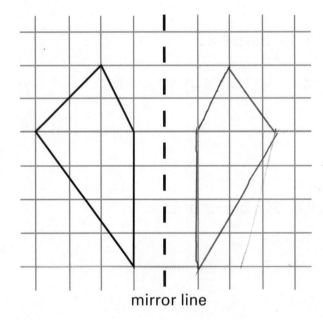

mirror line

(1 mark)

14 This table shows the heights of four children.

Complete the table.

	cm	m
Jake	150	1.50
Sue	139	1.39
Alice	115	1.15
Rosie	135	1.35

(2 marks) Q14

15 Calculate 5.7 – 2.15   3.65   *(1 mark)* Q15

16 Write in the missing digit to make this correct.

```
    3 2 4
  ×     □
  ─────────
  1 6 2 0
```

(1 mark) Q16

17 Draw two more straight sides to make a rectangle.

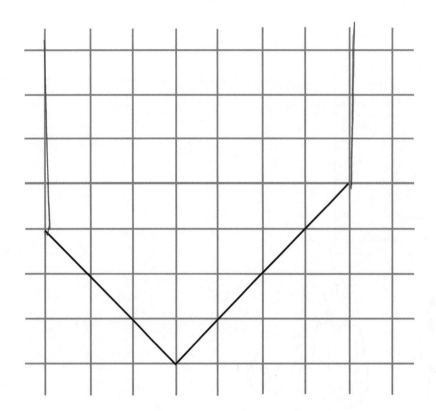

(1 mark)

18 Two of these numbers divide by 7 with no remainder.

Circle the two numbers.

17   24   28   31   37   49   *(1 mark)*

19 Calculate 35% of £560   £ ☐   *(1 mark)*

20 Here is a kite drawn on a graph:

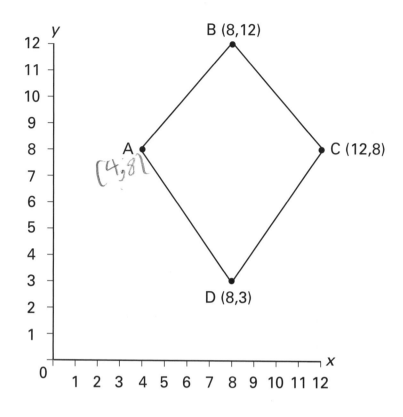

What are the coordinates of point A?

(4 , 8)

(1 mark)

Q20

21 Calculate 12.15 − 11.84   31

(1 mark)

Q21

$$\begin{array}{r} 1\overset{1}{2}.15 \\ 11.84 - \\ \hline 00.31 \\ \hline \end{array}$$

22 Jane has some rectangular tiles like this:

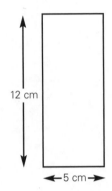

12 cm

←5 cm→

She then makes this T shape:

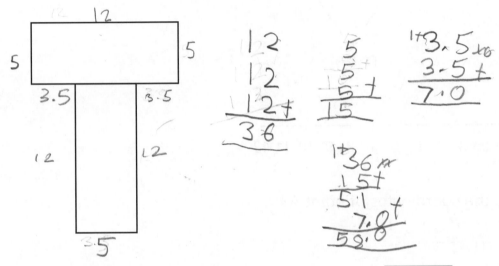

12

12	5	¹⁺3.5 ×6
12	5	3·5 +
12+	5+	7·0
36	15	

¹⁺36 ×
15 +
5·1
7·0 +
59·0

a) What is the perimeter of Jane's T shape? **58.0** cm   *(1 mark)*

She then puts two T shapes together.

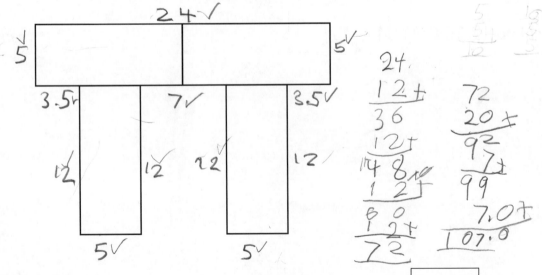

24.
12+	72
36	20+
12+	92
48×	7+
12+	99
80+	7.0+
12+	107·0
72	

b) What is the perimeter of Jane's new shape? **107.0** cm   *(1 mark)*

23 This is an isosceles triangle.

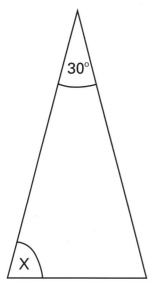

How many degrees is **angle x**? $\boxed{25}^{\circ}$

(1 mark)

24 Draw lines to match the circles which are equal in value.

3 × 4   7 × 8

9 × 10   18 × 2

14 × 4   5 × 18

6 × 6   6 × 2

(2 marks)

25 Calculate 1047 − 259 $\boxed{788}$

$$\begin{array}{r} 9\ 9\ {\overset{13}{\cancel{0}}}\ {\overset{17}{\cancel{4}}} \\ 2\ 5\ 9- \\ \hline 7\ 8\ 8 \end{array}$$

(1 mark)

26 Here are five shapes on a square grid:

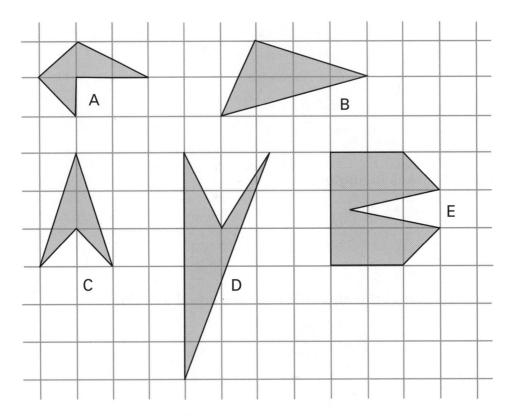

Write the letters of the **two** shapes which have a line of symmetry.

 and $\boxed{E}$

(2 marks)

27

This is the morning timetable for three school buses.

	PARK	SHOPS	POST OFFICE	SCHOOL
BUS 1	07:21	07:39	08:25	08:40
BUS 2	07:55	08:15	08:45	08:59
BUS 3	07:35	08:00	08:20	08:30

a) Which bus arrives at the post office **first**? Bus 3 *(1 mark)*

Q27a

b) How long in minutes does it take for **Bus 1** to get from the **park** to the **post office**? *(1 mark)*

Q27b

subtotal

28 Write each of the following numbers in the correct place on the Venn diagram below.

18   36   26

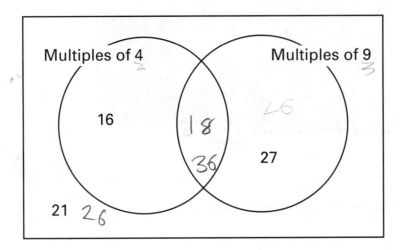

Multiples of 4   Multiples of 9

16   1 8   2 6
              3 6   27

21   26

(2 marks)

29 Here is a sorting diagram for numbers.

Write a number greater than 50 but less than 200 in each space.

	odd	**not** odd
a multiple of 9	6 3	5 4
a multiple of 7	7 7	5 6

(2 marks)

END OF TEST

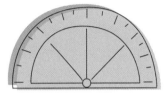

Test Paper 2 (calculator allowed)

Instructions:

- find a quiet place where you can sit down and complete the test paper undisturbed
- make sure you have all the necessary equipment to complete the test paper
- read the questions carefully
- answer all the questions in this test paper
- go through and check your answers when you have finished the test paper

Time:

This test paper is **45 minutes** long.

Note to Parents:

Check how your child has done against the Answers and Mark Scheme on pages 288–289.

Page	23	25	27	29	31	33	35	Max. Mark	**Actual Mark**
Score	....	....	....	....	....	....	....	40	....

First name   Jenna

Last name   George

1 Write the missing numbers in the boxes.

a) 264 ÷ 8 = 33 *(1 mark)*

b) 426 − 598 = 172 *(1 mark)*

c) 7 × 41 = 287 *(1 mark)*

2 Complete the diagram below to make a shape that is **symmetrical** about the **mirror line**.

You may use a mirror or tracing paper.

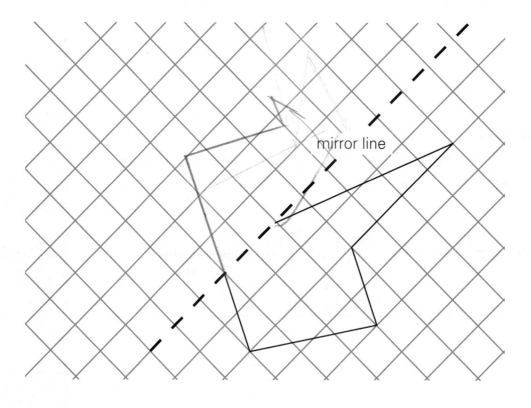

mirror line

(1 mark)

3 These are the opening times of the local newsagent.

	Opening times
Sunday	6am to 1pm
Monday	6am to 8pm
Tuesday	6am to 8pm
Wednesday	5:30am to 7pm
Thursday	5am to 12:30pm
Friday	6am to 10pm
Saturday	6am to 6:30pm

a) How many hours is the shop open on **Wednesday**?

(1 mark)

Q3a

b) On which day is the shop open the longest?  *(1 mark)*

Q3b

c) The newspapers are delivered to the shop at 7:30am every morning.

Molly arrives at the shop at ten to six on Thursday morning.

How many minutes does she have to wait until the newspapers arrive?

	minutes

(1 mark)

Q3c

subtotal

4 A shop sells stamps in packs of six and twelve.

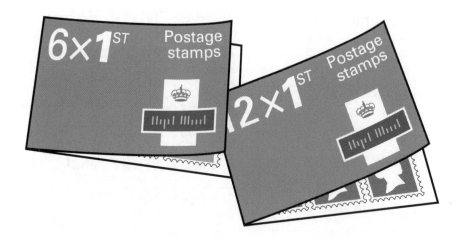

Charlie buys **three packs of six** and **one pack of twelve** stamps.

a) How many stamps did Charlie buy? | 30 | stamps *(1 mark)*

b) Jade bought some **packs of twelve** stamps.

She has **156** stamps altogether.

How many **packs of twelve** did Jade buy? | | packs *(1 mark)*

5 Write the missing numbers in the boxes.

a) | 692.52 | ÷ 17.4 = 39.8 *(1 mark)*

b) 463 − (19.25 − 11.8) = | 455.55 | *(1 mark)*

6 James has £20.

He buys two T-shirts and a pair of shorts.

£6.95

£3.75

How much money does he have left?   £ | 10.15

Show your working. You may get a mark.

£6.95 x2
£6.95 + x2
13.90

£13.90
£ 3.75 −
10.15

(2 marks)

Q6

subtotal

7 The number of children eating school dinners was recorded during one week in the summer term.

The results are shown on the graph below.

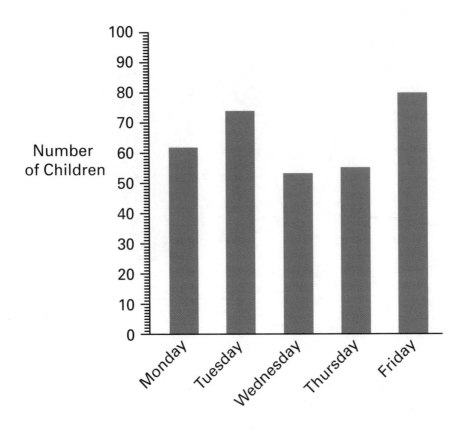

a) How many children ate school dinners on Monday?   60,2   *(1 mark)*

b) Which day of the week were there **27 fewer** children eating dinners than Friday?

   *(1 mark)*

8 Calculate $\frac{4}{7}$ of 399 [ ]

(1 mark)

9 Here are four quadrilaterals shown on a square grid:

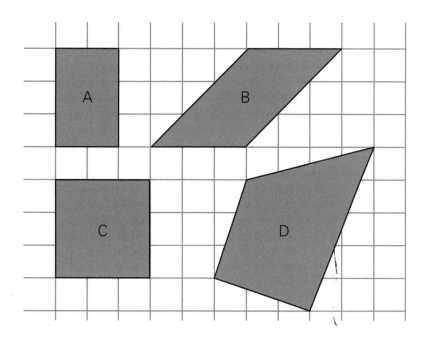

Write the letter of each quadrilateral in the correct area of the sorting diagram below.

One has been done for you.

	has 4 equal angles	has no right angle	has an obtuse angle
has 2 pairs of parallel sides	**C**	D	B
has 1 pair of parallel sides	A	D	B

(2 marks)

subtotal

10

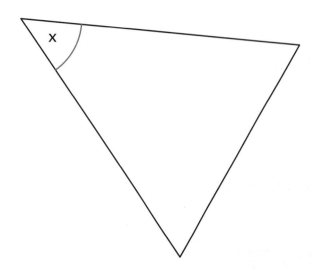

Measure **angle x** accurately.

Use an angle measurer (a protractor). °

(1 mark)

11 Sally makes a sequence of numbers.

Her rule is:

Multiply the previous number by two, then double it.

Write in the missing numbers of her sequence.

| 30 | 32 | 128 | 512 | 1024 | 8192 |

(2 marks)

12 An aeroplane takes off and its height above the ground is measured.
The results are shown on the graph below.

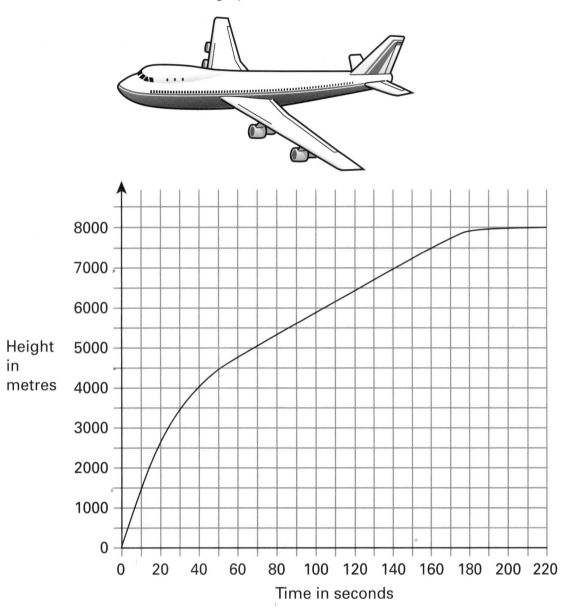

Height in metres

Time in seconds

a) Look at the graph. What was the
height of the plane after **50 seconds**? **4500** m   *(1 mark)*

Q12a

b) How long did it take
to get from **1500 m** to **7000 m**?   **120**   seconds

(1 mark)

Q12b

subtotal

13 Here is a rectangle with five identical squares inside it.

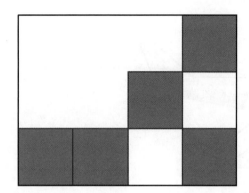

Not actual size

The **perimeter** of each square is 12 cm.

Calculate the **area** of the rectangle.

Show your working. You may get a mark.

area = ☐ sq cm

(2 marks)

14 Calculate 45% of 1440 ☐

(1 mark)

15 Write the missing numbers in the boxes.

a) [21] × 5 × 3 = 315   *(1 mark)* ☐ Q15a

b) (588 ÷ [   ]) + 27 = 111   *(1 mark)* ☐ Q15b

16 Here are some number cards:

7 7 7

8 8 8

Use **five** of the numbers to make this correct.

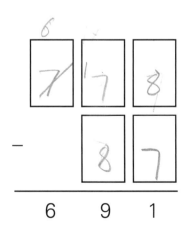

  6   9   1

(2 marks) ☐ Q16

17 A class of children are going to the seaside for a day trip. They will travel by train.

There are 29 children and 5 adults going on the trip. The total bill for the school is £250.50

Children   £188.50
Adults   £62.00
_____

Total   £250.50

a) How much does it cost for one adult?   £ ⬚   (1 mark)

b) What would be the total bill if an
   extra 7 children went on the trip?   £ 250.57

Show your working. You may get a mark.

a) £188.50
   £ 62.00 –
   £126.50

b) £ 188.50
          7↑
   £ch 188.57 ↖
   £   62.00 +↖
   £ 250.57

(2 marks)

18 This scale shows how heavy Mary is.

a) How **heavy** is Mary? kg

(1 mark)

Q18a

This scale shows the weight of Jay.

 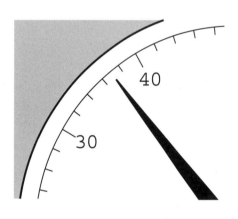

b) How much **lighter** than Mary is Jay? kg

(1 mark)

Q18b

19 Circle the number that is closest to 350.

129   97   420   (270)   235   *(1 mark)*

Q19

subtotal

20 Here is an isosceles triangle inside a rectangle:

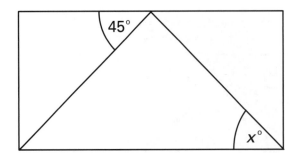

Not to scale.

Calculate the value of **angle x**. Do not use an angle measurer.

x = ⬚ °

(1 mark)

21 **n** stands for a whole number.

$6n - 8 = 34$

What is the value of **n**?　**n** = ⬚

(1 mark)

22 Put a tick (✔) in the correct box for each calculation.

	prime number	square number	negative number
(587 − 459) ÷ 2 _128_	✓		
(28.9 − 18.9) − 3 _10_			✓
(2.9 × 3.7) − 12 _10.73_		✓	
9 + (8 × 6) + 24 _48_	✓		

(2 marks)

Q22

END OF TEST

subtotal

Set A – Mental Arithmetic Test

The instructions and questions for this test are on page 296. The answers are on page 289.

Max. Mark	Actual Mark
20	....

Time: 5 seconds

1 [ ] ☐

2 [ ] 2p ☐

3 [ ] 30 790 ☐

4 [ ] ☐

5 [ ] ☐

11 [ ] mins $3\frac{1}{4}$ hrs ☐

12 [ ] 240 ☐

13 [ ] 25 ☐

14 [ ] 1.7 5 ☐

15 [ ] 30 40 50 ☐

Time: 10 seconds

6 £[ ] £5 80p ☐

7 [ ] 9 ☐

8 [ ] ☐

9 [ ] 0.9 ☐

10 [ ] cm 7 cm ☐

Time: 15 seconds

16 [ ] 15 34 22 ☐

17 [ ] 27 61 ☐

18 £[ ] 30% £35 ☐

19 [ ] 70 80 ☐

20 [ ]° 85° 190° ☐

Test Paper 1 (calculator **not** allowed)

Instructions:

- find a quiet place where you can sit down and complete the test paper undisturbed
- make sure you have all the necessary equipment to complete the test paper
- read the questions carefully
- answer all the questions in this test paper
- go through and check your answers when you have finished the test paper

Time:

This test paper is **45 minutes** long.

Note to Parents:

Check how your child has done against the Answers and Mark Scheme on pages 290–291.

Page	39	41	43	45	47	49	51	Max. Mark	**Actual Mark**
Score	....	....	....	....	....	....	....	40	....

First name Jenna

Last name George

1 Write the missing numbers below.

a) $(6 \times 5) - \boxed{43} = 13$ *(1 mark)*

b) $75 + \boxed{65} = 140$ *(1 mark)*

2 The start of a football match is shown on the clock below.

The kick-off time is delayed by 20 minutes.

What time does the match start? [ ] *(1 mark)*

3 Here is a parallelogram drawn on a graph:

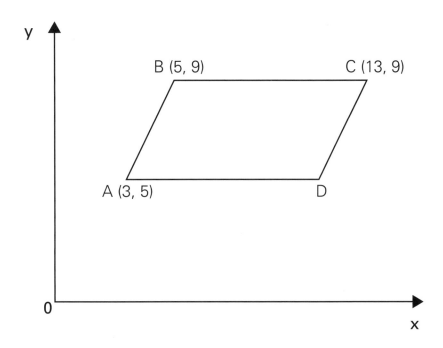

What are the coordinates of point D?

(☐ , ☐)

(1 mark) ☐
Q3

4 Complete the sequence below.

50 | 55 | 100   125 | ☐ | 175   200   *(1 mark)* ☐
Q4

subtotal

5 A shopkeeper kept a record of the different people that came into his shop on a Saturday. He put the results into a pie chart.

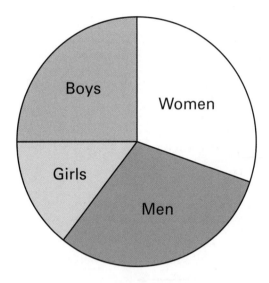

Total 120 people

a) Estimate the number of girls who entered the shop. | 20 | (1 mark)

b) Did more male or female people enter the shop? Circle your answer.

 MALE   FEMALE

Explain why you think this.

I think this, because if use your fingers then you will see that the boys have came into his shop ^more than the girls, and the Men and women are equal.

_____ (1 mark)

6 The highest daytime temperatures in London, New York and Paris for a day in March are shown below.

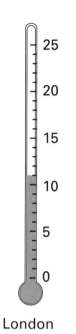

London

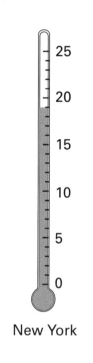

New York

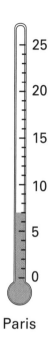

Paris

How many degrees warmer was it in New York than Paris? | 10,2 | °C

(1 mark)

Q6

7 Calculate   742 ÷ 14 | 53 |

Show your working. You may get a mark.

```
      0 53
  14 | 742
     - 7 0↓
       0 4 2
         4 2 -
       -------
         0 0
```

(2 marks)

Q7

subtotal

8 Look at the four number cards.

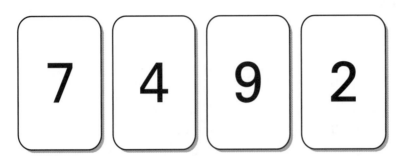

Choose **three** cards to make an **odd** number **greater than 500**.

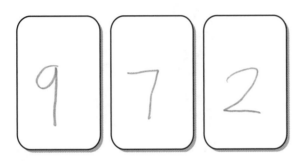

(1 mark)

9 Look at the diagram below. **Draw the line of symmetry of the shaded shape.**

You may use a mirror or tracing paper.

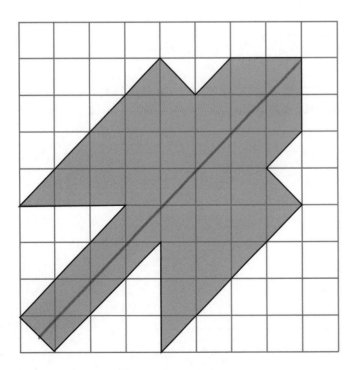

(1 mark)

10 Write in the missing digits.

| 2 | 9 | 7 | + | 4 | 8 | 7 | = | 7 | 8 | 4 |

(1 mark)

11 Look at this diagram:

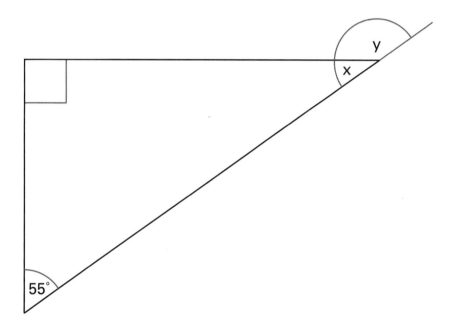

Calculate **angle x** and then calculate **angle y**.

Do not use a protractor.

a) X = [   ]°

(1 mark)

b) y = [   ]°

(1 mark)

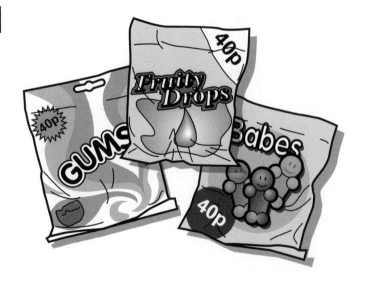

A bag of sweets weighs 120 grams and costs 40p.

a) How much do five bags of sweets cost?   £1.20   *(1 mark)*

Sally spends £1.60 on sweets.

b) What is the weight of Sally's sweets?   720

Show your working. You may get a mark.

40p
40p
40p +
£1.20

£1.60
   120 +
1.720

(2 marks)

13 This table shows the weights of four children.

Complete the table.

	grams	kilos
Amy	37 000	37
Alex	31 500	31.5
Ben	40 500	40.5
Charlie	37 020	37.02

(2 marks)

Q13

14 Here is an equilateral triangle inside a rectangle:

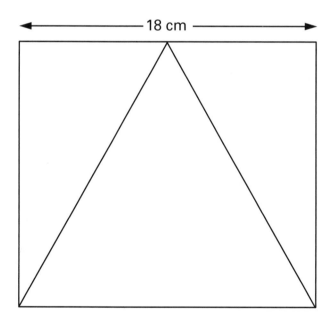

18 cm

What is the perimeter of the equilateral triangle? 34.2 cm *(1 mark)*

Q14

subtotal

15 Circle the **three** numbers that divide by 6 with no remainder.

47	48	49
50	51	52
53	54	55
56	57	58
59	60	61
62	63	64

(1 mark)

16

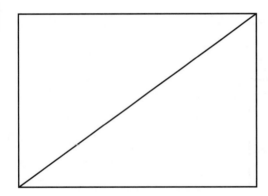

Measure accurately the length of the diagonal of this rectangle.

Give your answer in **centimetres**.   [   ] cm   *(1 mark)*

17 Calculate $20.04 - 18.98 =$ | 1.06 | *(1 mark)*

18 Calculate $\frac{3}{5}$ of $685 =$ | | *(1 mark)*

19 Draw the **reflection** of the shaded shape in the mirror line.

You may use a mirror or tracing paper.

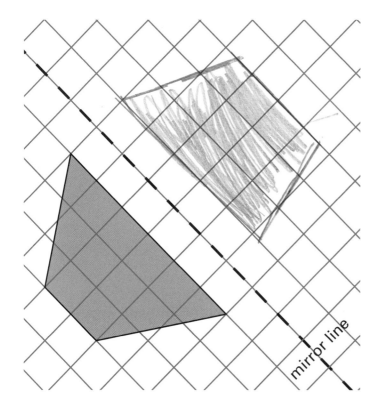

mirror line

(1 mark)

20 Calculate $1107 - 211$ | 896 | *(1 mark)*

21 Circle **all** the multiples of 7 in the list of numbers.

17   (21)   (35)   47   36   *(1 mark)*

22 Write each of the following numbers in the correct place on the Venn diagram below.

21   14   13

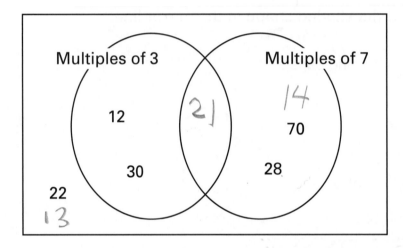

(2 marks)

23 Here is a sorting diagram for numbers.

Write a number greater than 20 but less than 100 in each space.

	even	square number
a multiple of 6	30	
a multiple of 8	32	

(2 marks)

24 Complete these fractions so that they are equivalent.

$$\frac{2}{4} \qquad \frac{1}{2} \qquad \frac{4}{8} \qquad \frac{}{32}$$

(2 marks)

Q24

25 There are 14 paint brushes in a box.

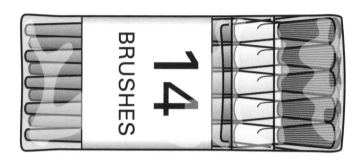

The school buys 21 boxes of brushes.

BRUSHES	BRUSHES	BRUSHES
BRUSHES	BRUSHES	BRUSHES
BRUSHES	BRUSHES	BRUSHES
BRUSHES	BRUSHES	BRUSHES
BRUSHES	BRUSHES	BRUSHES
BRUSHES	BRUSHES	BRUSHES
BRUSHES	BRUSHES	BRUSHES

How many brushes does the school buy? 294

Show your working. You may get a mark.

21
14 ✗
84
210 +
294

(2 marks)

Q25

subtotal

26 Harry weighs some sugar. He weighs 475 grams of sugar.

a) Draw an arrow on the scale to show 475 grams.

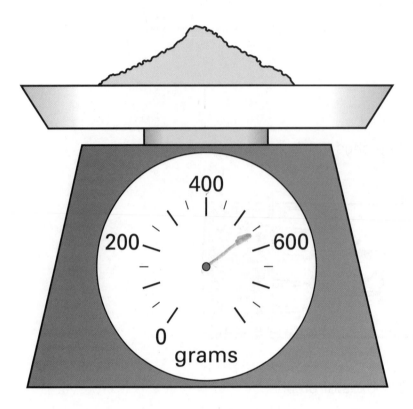

(1 mark)

b) How much more sugar does Sam need
to get a total of 1 kg of sugar?

grams   *(1 mark)*

27 Here are five shapes on a square grid:

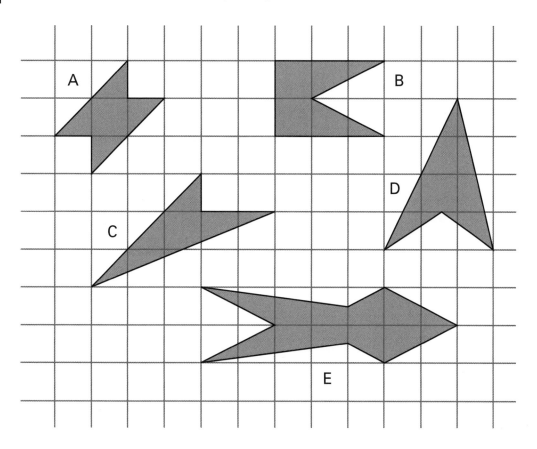

Write the letters of the **two** shapes which do **not** have a line of symmetry.

Shape C and Shape B

(2 marks)

Q27

END OF TEST

Set

B

KEY STAGE 2
Levels 3–5

Test Paper 2

Maths

Test Paper 2 (calculator allowed)

Test Paper 2 (calculator allowed)

Instructions:

- find a quiet place where you can sit down and complete the test paper undisturbed
- make sure you have all the necessary equipment to complete the test paper
- read the questions carefully
- answer all the questions in this test paper
- go through and check your answers when you have finished the test paper

Time:

This test paper is **45 minutes** long.

Note to Parents:

Check how your child has done against the Answers and Mark Scheme on pages 291–292.

Page	53	55	57	59	61	63	65	Max. Mark	**Actual Mark**
Score	....	....	....	....	....	....	....	40	....

First name ....

Last name ....

1 Circle the number that is closest to 900.

(850)   720   951   970   90   *(1 mark)*

Q1

2

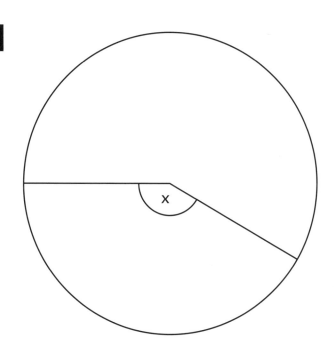

Measure the angle x accurately.

Use an angle measurer (a protractor).   ⁰   *(1 mark)*

Q2

subtotal

3 Show the correct time on the clocks below.

An example has been done for you.

half past three

a) quarter to six

(1 mark)

b) 11:25

(1 mark)

c) 23:45

(1 mark)

4 Write the missing numbers in the boxes.

a) $\boxed{301} \div 7 = 43$ *(1 mark)*

b) $539 - \boxed{650} = 111$ *(1 mark)*

c) $\boxed{9} \times 31 = 279$ *(1 mark)*

5 Here is a diagram for sorting numbers.

Write one number in each section of the diagram.

	more than 500	less than 500
multiple of 30	540	300
not a multiple of 30	1200	200

(2 marks)

6 These are the prices of some games at the school summer fair.

welly throwing	**45p**
lucky dip	**30p**
face painting	**£1.50**
dance mats	**£1.00**

Sally has **£5**. She has her **face painted** and then has **two**
tries at **welly throwing**. How much money does she have left? £ 2.69

Show your working. You may get a mark.

£5.'00   45p
£1.50   45p +
£3.50   90
   90 p
£2.69

(2 marks)

7 Calculate **80%** of **1680**   *(1 mark)*

8 Joe took part in a sponsored cycle ride.

This graph shows how far he rode and how long it took him.

9896.295

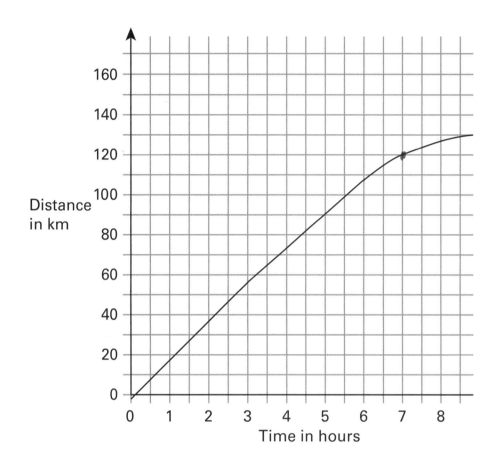

Distance in km

Time in hours

a) Look at the graph. How far had Joe ridden after seven hours?

120 km

(1 mark)

Q8a

b) Joe started riding at 8:30 in the morning. How far had he gone at 12:00pm?

km

(1 mark)

Q8b

9 Write the missing numbers in the boxes.

a) 502.35 ÷ 9896.295 = 19.7

(1 mark)

Q9a

25.85

b) (49.7 − 23.85) × 7 = 180.95

(1 mark)

Q9b

subtotal

10 On the grid below, draw a square with the same area as the shaded shape.

Use a ruler.

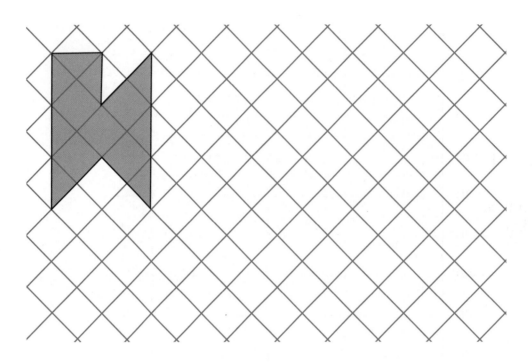

(1 mark)

11 Draw a line from each card to the correct part of the number line.

The first one has been done for you.

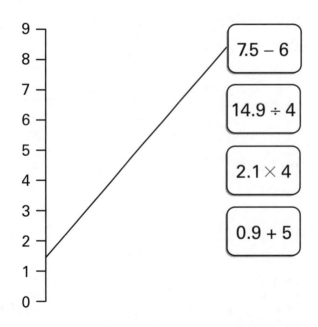

7.5 – 6

14.9 ÷ 4

2.1 × 4

0.9 + 5

(3 marks)

12   Calculate $\frac{2}{9}$ of 756   _(1 mark)_

13   At the supermarket eggs are for sale in boxes of six.

John needs 36 eggs for the egg and spoon race at school.

a) How many boxes of eggs does John need?   216   boxes   _(1 mark)_

John breaks $\frac{1}{3}$ of the eggs when he drops the boxes.

b) How many eggs does John break?   4   eggs   _(1 mark)_

subtotal

14 Complete the diagram below to make a shape that is **symmetrical** about the **mirror line**.

You may use a mirror or tracing paper.

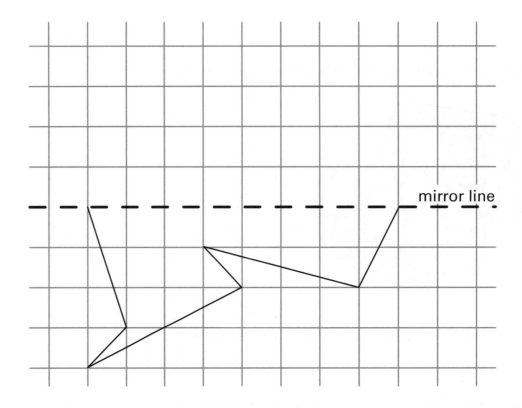

mirror line

(1 mark)

15 Harry makes a sequence of numbers.

His rule is:

Add seven to the previous number, then multiply by 3.

Write in the missing numbers of his sequence.

1   24   93   300   921   *(2 marks)*

16 Some children at school did a survey on the colour of their parents' cars.

The results of the survey are shown in the chart below.

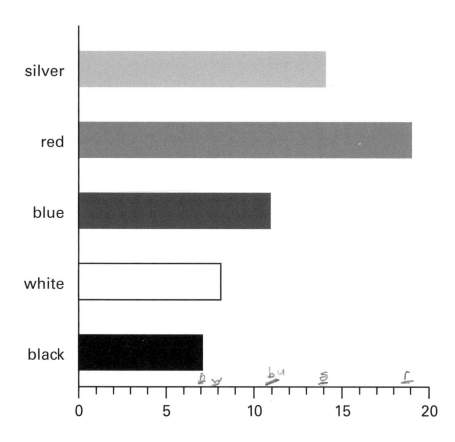

a) Which car colour has eight **more than** blue? [red] *(1 mark)* ☐ Q16a

b) What is the **total** number of cars in the survey? [49.4] *(1 mark)* ☐ Q16b

17 Write the missing numbers in the boxes.

a) 45
   $(5 \times 9) + 97 - 104 =$ [38] *(1 mark)* ☐ Q17a

b) [ ] $- 41 + 120 = 179$ *(1 mark)* ☐ Q17b

☐
subtotal

18 Write the temperature shown on the thermometer.

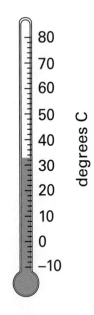

a) $\boxed{3.1\frac{1}{2}}$ °C

(1 mark)

Here is another thermometer:

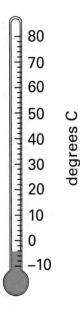

b) What is the difference between
the two temperature readings? $\boxed{}$ °C

(1 mark)

19

A box of twelve golf balls costs **£7.92**

a) How much does each ball cost?
 (1 mark)

Q19a

John wants eight golf balls and Tom wants four golf balls.

John and Tom both pay some money towards the golf balls.
Tom pays a third of the cost.

b) How much money does John pay? £

Show your working. You may get a mark.

£7.92
————
.91

(2 marks)

Q19b

subtotal

20 Here is a football pitch:

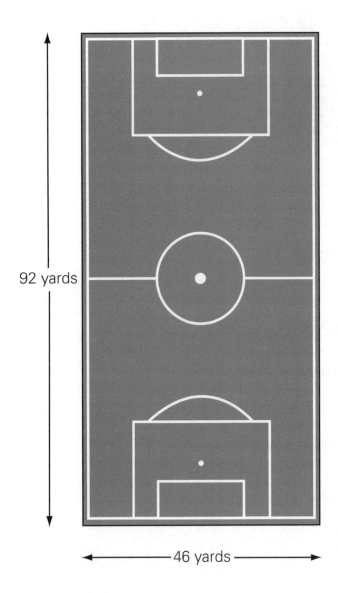

92 yards

← 46 yards →

One yard is **equivalent** to three feet.

What is the perimeter of the pitch? Give your answer in feet. ☐ feet

Show your working. You may get a mark.

(2 marks)

21 **t** and **r** each stand for a whole number.

r − **t** = 60

r is **four times** bigger than **t**.

Calculate the numbers for t and r.

Show your working. You may get a mark.

r = ☐   **t** = ☐

(2 marks) ☐

Q21

END OF TEST

Set B – Mental Arithmetic Test

The instructions and questions for this test are on page 297. The answers are on page 292.

Max. Mark	**Actual Mark**
20	....

Time: 5 seconds

1 [ ]   □

2 [ ] $\frac{3}{4}$ □

3 [ ]   70   2000   □

4 [ ]   70   □

5 [ ]   652   □

11 [ ]   cm   72 cm   □

12 [ ]   38%   □

13 [ ]   □

14 [ ]   100   110   □

15 [ ]   kg   2780 g   □

Time: 10 seconds

6 [ ] $1\frac{1}{4}$ $3\frac{1}{2}$ □

7 [ ]   7.3   □

8 [ ] $4z - 7$ □

9 [ ]   320   □

10 [ ]   □

Time: 15 seconds

16 [ ]   67   □

17 [ ]   8.3   12.4   □

18 £[ ]   £1.60   □

19 [ ]°   20°   85°   □

20 [ ]   18   □

Test Paper 1 (calculator **not** allowed)

Instructions:

- find a quiet place where you can sit down and complete the test paper undisturbed
- make sure you have all the necessary equipment to complete the test paper
- read the questions carefully
- answer all the questions in this test paper
- go through and check your answers when you have finished the test paper

Time:

This test paper is **45 minutes** long.

Note to Parents:

Check how your child has done against the Answers and Mark Scheme on pages 293–294.

Page	69	71	73	75	77	79	80	Max. Mark	**Actual Mark**
Score	....	....	....	....	....	....	....	40	....

First name ....

Last name ....

1 Write the missing number in the box.

$$7 \times \boxed{} = 350$$

(1 mark)

2 Calculate $532 - 167$ $\boxed{}$

(1 mark)

3 Complete these fractions so that they are equivalent.

$$\frac{}{6} \qquad \frac{}{3} \qquad \frac{}{27} \qquad \frac{}{15}$$

(2 marks)

4 DVDs are on offer at the supermarket. The sign says:

1 DVD is £17.99 or buy 2 DVDs for £30

How much money will Sarah save if she buys
two DVDs together instead of buying them separately? £ $\boxed{}$ *(1 mark)*

5 Circle **two** numbers which add to make **0.29**

0.4   0.04   0.13   0.15   0.25   0.09   *(1 mark)*

Q5

6 Calculate 1245 – 351 ☐   *(1 mark)*

Q6

7 John has some bricks. Each brick is 10 cm long, 4 cm high and 4 cm deep.

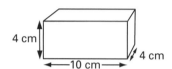

John then builds a square wall using eight bricks like this:

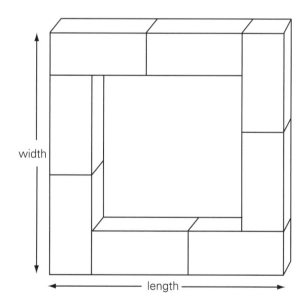

a) What is the perimeter of the wall?   ☐ cm   *(1 mark)*

Q7a

b) Calculate the inside perimeter of the wall.   ☐ cm   *(1 mark)*

Q7b

subtotal

8 Below is a trapezium with a design on it.

The trapezium is reflected in the mirror line.

Complete the reflected design.

You may use a mirror or tracing paper.

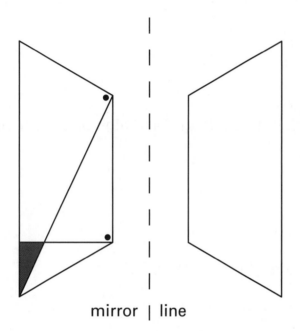

mirror | line

(1 mark)

9 Write in the missing digits.

| 3 | 3 | | + | 5 | | 6 | = | 9 | 2 | 5 |

(1 mark)

10 Mr Green has three tubs of water.

He weighs them on the garden scales.

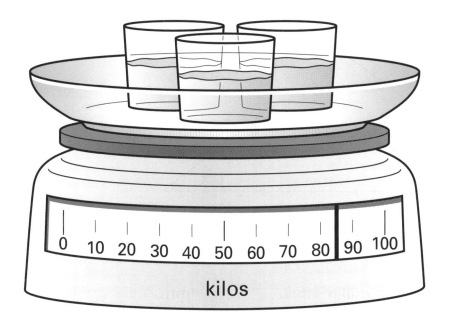

What is the reading on the scale? *(2 marks)*

11 Which of these numbers give 90 when rounded to the nearest 10?

Circle **all** the correct numbers.

88   97   74   92   86   91   *(1 mark)*

subtotal

12 Measure accurately the **shortest side** of this shape.

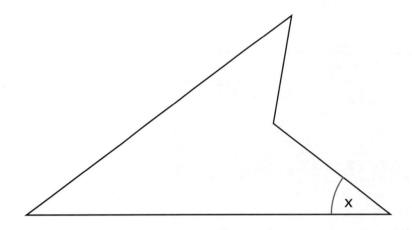

a) Give your answer in **millimetres**. mm (1 mark)

b) Measure **angle x** using a protractor. ° (1 mark)

13 Calculate 954 ÷ 9 (1 mark)

14 Here is an equilateral triangle inside a square:

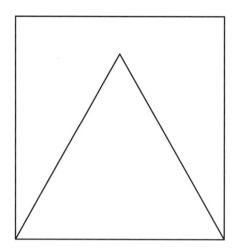

Not actual size.

The perimeter of the square is 72 centimetres.

What is the perimeter of the triangle? cm

Show your working. You may get a mark.

(2 marks)

Q14

15 Write in the missing digits to make this correct.

```
   □ 8 □
 + 5 3 7
 ───────
   7 2 1
```

(1 mark)

Q15

subtotal

16 Circle **all** the multiples of 6 in the list of numbers.

23   30   46   48   60   *(1 mark)*

17 Draw the **reflection** of the shaded shape in the mirror line.

You may use a mirror or tracing paper.

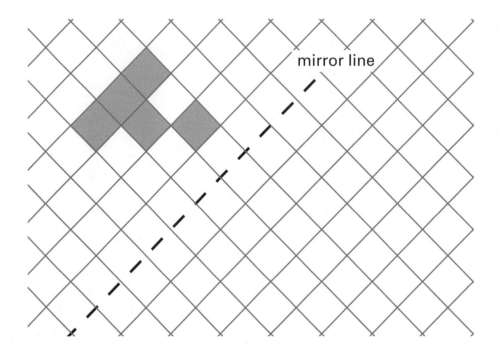

(1 mark)

18 Calculate $64.09 + 39.78$ [   ]   *(1 mark)*

19 This table shows the increase in train fares.

Train fares	
Old fare	New fare
£25.00	£27.50
£28.75	£33.00
£40.00	£44.75
£43.50	£50.00
£47.75	£51.25
£49.00	£58.00
£51.00	£61.50

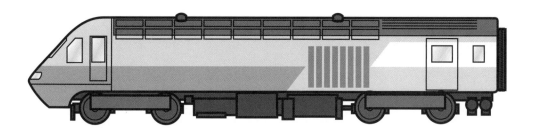

a) Jack's new fare is £51.25
   How much has his fare increased?   £ ⬚   *(1 mark)*   ⬚
                                                            Q19a

b) Jane's new fare is £9 more than her old fare.
   What is her new fare?   £ ⬚   *(1 mark)*   ⬚
                                                  Q19b

subtotal

20 Circle **two** different numbers which multiply together to make 2 million.

10   500   2000   40 000   200 000   *(1 mark)*

21 Here is a square divided into identical smaller squares:

What percentage of the square is shaded? ☐ %   *(1 mark)*

22 This table shows the lengths of four pencils.

Complete the table.

	mm	cm
pencil 1	230	23
pencil 2	195	
pencil 3		18
pencil 4		17.4

(2 marks)

Q22

23 Calculate 9.23 – 8.94 [   ]

(1 mark)

Q23

24 Write each of the following numbers in the correct place on the Venn diagram below.

15   35   53

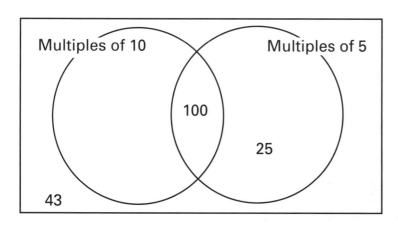

(2 marks)

Q24

subtotal

25 Calculate 5% of £1800   £ [ ]

(1 mark)

26 Here is a sorting diagram for numbers.

Write a number less than 200 in each space.

	even	odd
divides by 5 with no remainder		
divides by 11 with no remainder		

(2 marks)

27 Jack and Mary are going to the cinema to watch a film. The film starts at **twenty minutes to eight.**

Complete the clock below to show the time that the film starts.

(1 mark)

28 Three children have £2 each.

Ellie   Josh   Ben

Ben gives Josh $\frac{1}{4}$ of his money.

a) **How much money do Josh and Ben have now?**

Josh £ ⬚

Ben £ ⬚

(1 mark)

Q28a

b) Ellie spends 50% of her money and gives the remainder to Ben.

How much money does Ben have now?

Ben £ ⬚

(1 mark)

Q28b

subtotal

29 The children in Year 5 go on a class trip to a theme park.

There are 40 children in Year 5 and four teachers go on the trip as well.

What is the total cost for the group to enter the theme park? £

Show your working. You may get a mark.

(2 marks)

END OF TEST

Test Paper 2 (calculator allowed)

Instructions:

- find a quiet place where you can sit down and complete the test paper undisturbed
- make sure you have all the necessary equipment to complete the test paper
- read the questions carefully
- answer all the questions in this test paper
- go through and check your answers when you have finished the test paper

Time:

This test paper is **45 minutes** long.

Note to Parents:

Check how your child has done against the Answers and Mark Scheme on pages 294–295.

Page	83	85	87	89	91	93	95	Max. Mark	**Actual Mark**
Score	....	....	....	....	....	....	....	40	....

First name _____

Last name _____

1 Complete the diagram below to make a shape that is **symmetrical** about the **mirror line**.

You may use a mirror or tracing paper.

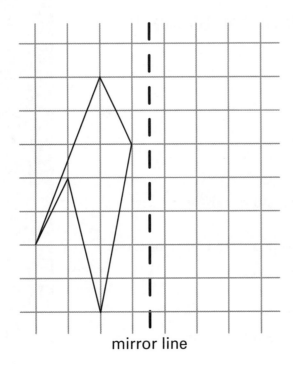

mirror line

(1 mark)

2 Circle the number that is closest to 115.

85   150   215   515   511   *(1 mark)*

3 Flower seeds are available in packs of 40 seeds and packs of 100 seeds.

Sally needs 960 seeds for a display in her garden.

There are only six packs of 100 seeds available in the shop.

What is the smallest number of packs Sally can buy from the shop to get 960 seeds?

Show your working. You may get a mark.

(2 marks)

Q3

4 The amount of rainfall was measured during last year.

Here is a chart showing the information recorded:

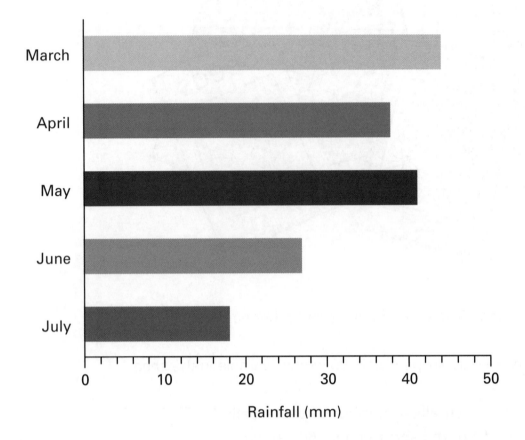

Rainfall (mm)

a) How much rainfall was there in **June**? ⬚ mm   *(1 mark)*

b) How much more rainfall was there in **March** than **July**? ⬚ mm

(1 mark)

5 Write in the missing numbers.

a) $279.3 = (39.9 \times \boxed{})$ *(1 mark)*

b) $980 - (85.9 \times 7.4) = \boxed{}$ *(1 mark)*

6 These are the prices of snacks at the school disco.

small soda	50p
large soda	75p
crisps	35p
chocolate bar	40p

Jack has **£3**; he wants to buy three large sodas, two chocolate bars and three bags of crisps.

How much **more** money does Jack need?   £ [   ]

Show your working. You may get a mark.

(2 marks)

Q6

subtotal

7 A number sequence has the rule:

Take 6 away from the previous number, then add 18.

Complete the number sequence using this rule.

13 ☐ ☐ ☐ *(2 marks)*

8 Here is a clock:

a) What time was it 50 minutes ago? ☐ *(1 mark)*

Here is another clock:

18:38

b) What time is it in 35 minutes? ☐ *(1 mark)*

9   Calculate 30% of 390   ☐   *(1 mark)* ☐

10   Here is a shape on a square grid:

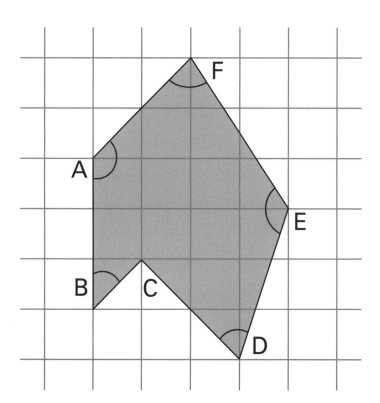

For each sentence, put a tick (✔) if it is true. Put a cross (✘) if it is untrue.

Line **CD** is parallel to line **EF**.   ☐

Line **BC** is parallel to line **AF**.   ☐

Angle **F** is a right angle.   ☐

Angle **E** is obtuse.   ☐   *(2 marks)* ☐

11 Jack has three cans of fizzy drink.

He pours all three cans into a jug.

a) Draw the correct level on the jug below.

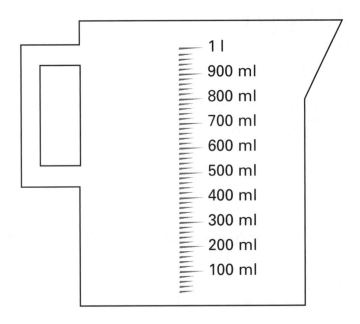

(1 mark)

Jack shares the fizzy drink between six children.

b) How much fizzy drink will they have each? ⬚ ml   *(1 mark)*

12

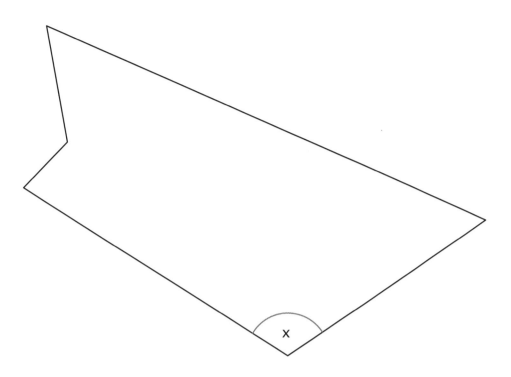

Measure angle x accurately.

Use an angle measurer (a protractor).

[   ]°

(1 mark)

13   Here is a diagram for sorting numbers.

Write one number in each section of the diagram.

	less than 200	more than 200
even number that divides by 7		
odd number that divides by 7		

(2 marks)

14 Here is an equilateral triangle with four smaller equilateral triangles inside it.

The shaded triangle has a perimeter of 27 cm.

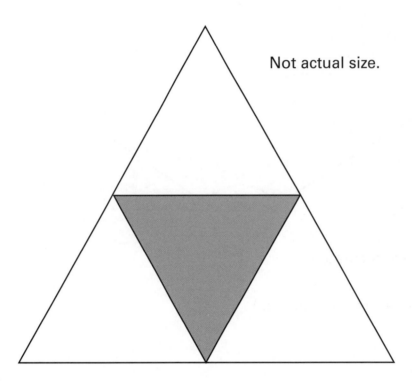

Not actual size.

What is the perimeter of the large equilateral triangle? ☐ cm

Show your working. You may get a mark.

(2 marks)

15 Write in the missing numbers.

a) 913 − ☐ = 471 *(1 mark)*

Q15a

b) ☐ × 89 = 356 *(1 mark)*

Q15b

16 Water was heated up during a science lesson.

The temperature was recorded and the time taken throughout the experiment. The results are shown on the graph below.

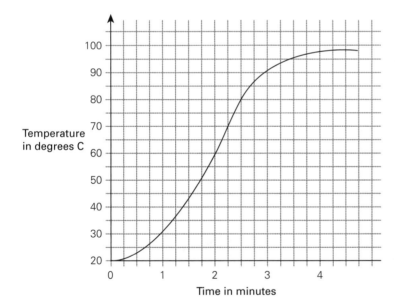

a) Read from the graph. How long does it take for the temperature to reach 80°C? ☐ minutes *(1 mark)*

Q16a

b) Use the graph to work out how many degrees the water heated up from one to three minutes. ☐ °C *(1 mark)*

Q16b

subtotal

17 Calculate $\frac{5}{8}$ of 576 [ ] *(1 mark)*

18 Write in the missing number.

([ ] × 9) ÷ 4 = 36 *(1 mark)*

19 Here are two regular octagons with shaded triangles inside them.

Under each octagon put a circle around the correct name of the shaded triangle.

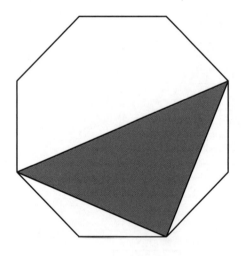

scalene   scalene

equilateral   equilateral

isosceles   isosceles   *(2 marks)*

20 Eighteen people go bowling together.

Adults £2.99 per game

Children £1.99 per game

There are six adults and twelve children.

a) How much does it cost altogether for one game?   £ ☐

Show your working. You may get a mark.

(2 marks)   ☐ Q20a

Drinks cost 55p each.

b) How many people had a drink if they spent £7.15?   ☐   *(1 mark)*   ☐ Q20b

subtotal ☐

21 Here is a regular pentagon:

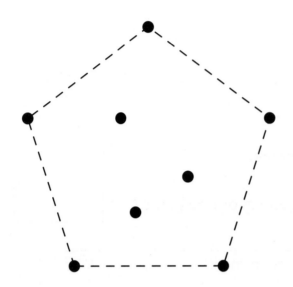

a) Join any three of the dots to make a scalene triangle.   *(1 mark)*

Here is a square:

b) Draw an isosceles triangle inside the square. All corners of the triangle must touch the edge of the square.

Use a ruler.   *(1 mark)*

22 **x**, **y** and **z** each stand for a whole number.

x + **y** + **z** = 160

z is **three times** bigger than **x**.

y is **ten greater** than **x**.

Calculate the numbers **x**, **y** and **z**.

Show your working. You may get a mark.

X = ☐

y = ☐

z = ☐

(3 marks) ☐

Q22

END OF TEST

Set C – Mental Arithmetic Test

The instructions and questions for this test are on page 298. The answers are on page 295.

Max. Mark	**Actual Mark**
20	....

Time: 5 seconds

1 [ ] □

2 [ ] ml □

3 [ ] □

4 [ ] : [ ] □

5 [ ] 56 □

Time: 10 seconds

6 [ ] 80   470 □

7 [ ] 64 □

8 [ ] 370 □

9 [ ] 800 □

10 [ ] mins $10\frac{3}{4}$ hrs □

11 [ ] m   128 m □

12 [ ] 300 □

13 [ ] □

14 [ ] 900 □

15 [ ] mins □

Time: 15 seconds

16 [ ] 47   95 □

17 [ ] 4.7 □

18 £ [ ] £14   £8 □

19 £ [ ] £1.08 □

20 [ ] 90   70 □

Notes

Set
A

KEY STAGE 2
Levels 3–5

Reading
Test Paper

English

On Track

Reading Test Paper

On Track

Instructions:

- find a quiet place where you can sit down and complete the test paper undisturbed
- make sure you have all the necessary equipment to complete the test paper
- read the questions carefully
- answer all the questions in this test paper
- go through and check your answers when you have finished the test paper

Time:

This test paper is **1 hour** long.

You should ensure you spend **15 minutes** reading through the Reading Material on pages 15–26 before you begin the test. Do not worry if you have not read all the Reading Material in this time, because you can (and should) look at it as many times as you like during the test.

The main written part of the test should take **45 minutes**. There are several question types:

Multiple choice	you put a ring around the correct option
Short answers	requiring only a word or short phrase
Several line answers	these questions require you to write more than a single point
Explanation answers	you are required to write an answer and explain it, often in quite a lot of detail and with evidence from the text
Other answers	you may be required to draw lines connecting related words

Check how your child has done against the Answers and Mark Scheme on pages 299–301.

Page	111	113	115	117	119	121	Max. Mark	**Actual Mark**
Score	....	....	....	....	....	....	50	....

First name _____

Last name _____

ON TRACK

Contents

Introduction

Since the early nineteenth century, people have had a fascination with trains and rail travel. From the early trains to the present day, this mode of transport has played a huge role in the daily life of nations around the globe.

Due to rail travel, trade and industry changed as it provided a faster way to transport large quantities of goods and materials. Our lives changed, because of the ease with which we could visit new and distant places with greater speed than ever before.

The railway age has influenced many books and films. *The Railway Children* is one such book. Written at the beginning of the twentieth century, it has also been turned into several film versions. You can read an extract from the book and all about the films on the following pages.

Other information here provides a brief history of the development of rail travel and an insight into The Orient Express, considered by many to be the world's most luxurious train.

After their father goes away unexpectedly, Bobbie, Peter and Phyllis move to the countryside with their mother. They leave behind their life in London to live in a small cottage called Three Chimneys.

They had lived all their lives in a street where cabs and omnibuses rumbled by at all hours, and the carts of butchers and bakers and candlestick makers might occur at any moment. Here in the deep silence of the sleeping country the only things that went by were the trains. They seemed to be all that was left to link the children to the old life that had once been theirs. Straight down the hill in front of Three Chimneys the daily passage of their six feet began to mark a path across the crisp, short turf. They began to know the hours when certain trains passed, and they gave names to them. The 9.15 up was called the Green Dragon. The 10.07 down was the Worm of Wantley. The midnight town express, whose shrieking rush they sometimes woke from their dreams to hear, was the Fearsome Fly-by-night. Peter got up once, in chill starshine, and, peeping at it through his curtains, named it on the spot.

It was by the Green Dragon that the old gentleman travelled. He was a very nice-looking old gentleman, and he looked as if he were nice, too, which is not at all the same thing. He had a fresh-coloured, clean-shaven face and white hair, and he wore rather odd-shaped collars and a top-hat that wasn't exactly the same kind as other people's. Of course the children didn't see all this at first. In fact the first thing they noticed about the old gentleman was his hand.

Th

It was one morning as they sat on the fence waiting for the Green Dragon, which was three and a quarter minutes late by Peter's Waterbury watch that he had had given him on his last birthday.

"The Green Dragon's going where Father is," said Phyllis; "if it were a really real dragon, we could stop it and ask it to take our love to Father."

"Dragons don't carry people's love," said Peter; "they'd be above it."

"Yes, they do, if you tame them thoroughly first. They fetch and carry like pet spaniels," said Phyllis, "and feed out of your hand. I wonder why Father never writes to us."

"Mother says he's been too busy," said Bobbie, "but he'll write soon, she says."

"I say," Phyllis suggested, "let's all wave to the Green Dragon as it goes by. If it's a magic dragon, it'll understand and take our loves to Father. And if it isn't, three waves aren't much. We shall never miss them."

So when the Green Dragon tore shrieking out of the mouth of its dark lair, which was the tunnel, all three children stood on the railing and waved their pocket-handkerchiefs without stopping to think whether they were clean handkerchiefs or the reverse. They were, as a matter of fact, very much the reverse.

And out of a first-class carriage a hand waved back. A quite clean hand. It held a newspaper. It was the old gentleman's hand.

After this it became the custom for waves to be exchanged between the children and the 9.15.

And the children, especially the girls, liked to think that perhaps the old gentleman knew Father, and would meet him "in business", wherever that shady retreat might be, and tell him how his three children stood on a rail far away in the green country and waved their love to him every morning, wet or fine.

From *The Railway Children* by Edith Nesbit

reen Dragon
d the Old Gentleman

The *Railway*
From Book to Screen

The book

The Railway Children tells the tale of Roberta, Peter and Phyllis as they embark on a series of adventures. They are forced to move to a country cottage when their father unexpectedly goes away from their London home. In their new surroundings they become fascinated by the nearby railway and meet many new friends as they wonder where their father is and whether he will ever return.

Author Edith Nesbit based some of the ideas in the story on her own experiences. Her first children's book, *The Treasure Seekers*, was published in 1899. *The Railway Children* was published seven years later in 1906 and is still extremely popular today.

Children

On screen

The Railway Children was first shown in 1968 as a six-part serial on BBC television. The serial was made in black and white. A 16 year-old girl called Jenny Agutter played the role of Roberta (Bobbie).

In 1970 the story was released in a very well-known film version, this time in colour. Again the role of Bobbie was played by Jenny Agutter.

The first showing (the premiere) took place in London in 1970 with special guests including Her Royal Highness Princess Margaret, accompanied by her nephews Prince Andrew and Prince Edward.

At Christmas 1970, it was shown privately to the Queen and other members of the Royal Family at Windsor Castle.

The British Film Institute has voted *The Railway Children* among the best one hundred British pictures of the past century. It has also been included in the Chicago Museum of Fine Arts as an example of fine British film making.

In 2000, a new film version was released. This immediately proved very popular with old and new fans alike. The role of Bobbie was this time played by Jemima Rooper, but there remained a strong link with the original film; the mother was played by Jenny Agutter.

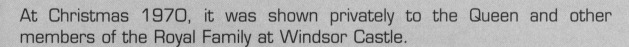

An Interview With the Railway Children

It was a rather wet and dismal Thursday when I went to the set of *The Railway Children* (2000 film) at Horsted Keynes in Sussex to meet the three young stars of the production, Jemima, Jack and Clare.

They were sitting in a caravan in their Edwardian costumes looking just like children from another world, but talking very much like the modern children they are.

Have you read E. Nesbit's book?

Jemima: I read it when I was very young as it's one of those classic books everyone reads. I read it again when I was auditioning for the part of Bobbie so I could research the character.

Clare: I once started to read it but didn't finish it but then, when I got the part of Phyllis, I had to complete a book-reading exercise for school so I read it then.

Jack: I haven't read it all, but I have heard it on tape and I've seen the 1970 film.

Have you found your characters easy to play?

Jemima: I do now but at first I was worried, because playing a twelve year-old in the early 1900s is very different. They were very much children then until they were quite a lot older.

Clare: Phyllis is pretty easy to play, because she's quite young and hasn't learnt much about the world yet. She doesn't have any major speeches using large, old-fashioned words.

Jack: Playing Peter is quite straightforward. I think he's trying to be grown up and be the man of the house. He's not really that big, but would like to take control.

Have you noticed any similarities between your characters and yourselves?

Jemima: Bobbie is lovely and she's one of those people you admire and want to be like. She is very sweet and gentle with her brother and sister. She's very amusing trying to be adult and mature. I'd like to think we were similar, but really I don't think so! Jack, Clare and I feel like real brother and sisters, which is nice. I definitely feel like their older sister. But no, I don't think I'm really like Bobbie at all.

Did wearing the period costumes help towards playing the character?

Jemima: Absolutely! It really, really helps! The minute you've got your costume on your movements are restricted. It makes me feel like a little doll, which makes me feel younger and helps with the part.

Jack: Most of the costumes are alright, but at the moment I am having problems with this stiff collar! It's kind of hard to breathe sometimes. I think wearing the costumes does help you to focus.

At this point a member of the production team entered the caravan and called the children out into the damp morning, ready to bring to life another scene from E. Nesbit's classic story.

The interviewer was Pete Coleman

A Sma

For centuries, the fastest way of travelling was on horseback. Long-distance travel meant many days, many rests and often many changes of horse. People rarely travelled more than a few kilometres from their homes and very few visited other towns or villages.

When railways came along in the 1800s, all of this changed. Travel became quick and convenient. Major towns and cities throughout Great Britain and the rest of Europe became easy to reach in just a few hours. People could move around the world as never before and trains became as popular then as air travel is today.

The world's first public steam railway, just 40 km of track in north-east England, was soon followed by larger networks and rail travel opened up new horizons for everyone. People started to make day trips, with the seaside especially popular, and large continents could be crossed in just a few days rather than months.

Fact Box

- Longest railway network – the USA with 240,000 km

- Longest railway – the Trans-Siberian line from Moscow to Vladivostok (9,611 km)

- Longest straight track – 478 km in south-western Australia

1804 Richard Trevithick tests the first steam locomotive in Wales.

1825 The Stockton to Darlington Railway opens using steam locomotives.

1863 The world's first underground passenger railway opens in London.

1883 The Orient Express first runs from Paris to Bucharest.

World

Speeding into the future

The first trains were powered by steam. In 1829, the Rocket could average 24 km per hour. Soon, however, bigger and faster steam locomotives came along. In the 1870s the Stirling Single could reach speeds of 129 km per hour and in 1893, an American locomotive was said to have travelled at 160 km per hour.

Another famous British train, the Mallard, reached 203 km per hour in 1938. By now, though, diesel and electrically powered trains were also becoming popular. The age of steam was slowly coming to an end.

From Rocket ...

The Rocket was the brainchild of Robert and George Stephenson. In 1829, the Rainhill Trials were held to find the best locomotive for the Liverpool to Manchester railway. It convinced people that steam locomotives were the future of transport.

... to Bullet

The Bullet entered service in 1964, running between Tokyo and Osaka in Japan. Shaped more like a bullet than a train, the latest version reaches speeds of 300 km per hour (186 mph).

1938 The Mallard sets the world speed record of 203 km per hour.

1964 The Bullet enters service in Japan.

1981 The high speed French TGV enters service between Paris and Lyon.

1994 The 50 km long Channel Tunnel is completed, linking Britain with the rest of Europe.

The Venice Simplon Orient Express is the most famous luxury train in the world. It has been used by the rich and famous since its first journey in 1883. Glamour, elegance and style apply to both the train and its passengers.

On board, passengers have their own personal stewards attending to their every need. Wood-panelled compartments provide private sitting rooms by day and luxurious bedrooms by night.

A dining car is laid out with the finest crystal glasses, table linen and cutlery awaiting the service of wonderful food produced by French chefs.

In the evening, passengers wearing fine gowns and suits gather to sip drinks as they chat or listen to the piano in the bar.

All this takes place as the train snakes its way across Europe and if the quality of life inside the train becomes too much, the passengers can simply look through the window at some of the finest scenery the continent has to offer.

A journey on the Orient Express is a journey on which standards are beyond the ordinary. Wealthy passengers travel in luxury through a rich and varied landscape on what is seen by many to be the most romantic journey in the world.

Travelling in Style

Section 1

These questions are about the fiction passage "The Green Dragon and the Old Gentleman" on pages 102–103.

Choose the best word or group of words and put a ring around your choice.   *(1 mark)*

☐ Q1

1   The old gentleman travelled on:

the midnight town express.

the Green Dragon.

the 10.07 down.

the Fearsome Fly-by-night.

2   The first thing the children noticed about the old gentleman was: *(1 mark)*

☐ Q2

his hat.

his newspaper.

his hand.

his white hair.

3   Phyllis suggested that they all: *(1 mark)*

☐ Q3

watch for trains.

go to the station.

wave to the old man.

wave to the Green Dragon.

☐ subtotal

4   The children liked to think that the old gentleman would: (1 mark)

take their love to father.

wave to them.

be their friend.

be kind to them.

5   Phyllis told the others that dragons: (1 mark)

could be fierce creatures.

could be treated like a pet.

are easy to train.

knew their father.

6   The trains ... *seemed to be all that was left to link the children to the old life that had once been theirs.* Give two reasons why the trains provided this link.   (2 marks)

a) _____

_____

_____

_____

b) _____

_____

_____

_____

7   *... when the Green Dragon tore shrieking out of the mouth of its dark lair ...*

Why does the author use these words to describe the dragon coming
out of the tunnel?   *(2 marks)*

_____

_____

_____

_____

8   How can you tell that the children are missing their father?

Explain fully, using the text to help you.   *(3 marks)*

_____

_____

_____

_____

_____

_____

9   When the children waved at the train they used their pocket-handkerchiefs.

a) Why did they wave with their handkerchiefs?   (1 mark)

_____

_____

_____

b) Why do you think they did not stop ... *to think whether they were clean*
   handkerchiefs?   (1 mark)

_____

_____

_____

10 *"Mother says he's been too busy," said Bobbie, "but he'll write soon, she says."*

Explain what this tells us about Bobbie's relationship with her brother and sister.
                                                                  (1 mark)

_____

_____

_____

Section 2

These questions are about the information in "*The Railway Children –*
From Book to Screen" on pages 104–105.

11 Why has the title "*The Railway Children* – From Book to Screen" been chosen for
this short, informative text? *(1 mark)*

Q11

_____

_____

_____

12 What is the purpose of this piece of text? *(1 mark)*

Q12

_____

_____

_____

13 The text shows that the 1970 film version of *The Railway Children* was very highly
thought of. Select two pieces of information in the text that show this. *(2 marks)*

Q13

a) _____

_____

_____

b) _____

_____

_____

subtotal

Section 3

These questions are about the text "An Interview With the Railway Children" on page 107.

14 Jemima tells us that she finds her character easy to play, but *".. at first I was worried, because playing a twelve year-old in the early 1900s is very different. They were very much children then until they were quite a lot older."*

What does she mean by
"They were very much children then until they were quite a lot older"? *(2 marks)*

_____

_____

_____

_____

15 Why are the children described as
"… looking just like children from another world"? *(1 mark)*

_____

_____

_____

16 How does Jemima think that wearing her costume helps her to play the part of Bobbie? *(1 mark)*

_____

_____

_____

Section 4

17 The title of the section on pages 108 and 109 is "A Small World".

Explain why this is a suitable title for this section. *(3 marks)*

☐ Q17

_____

_____

_____

_____

_____

_____

18 Put the following information in the correct order. The first one has been done for you. *(2 marks)*

☐ Q18

The Japanese Bullet train makes its first journey   ☐

The Rocket wins the Rainhill Trials   ☐

The Mallard sets the world record   ☐

Trevithick tests the first steam locomotive   ☐ 1

subtotal

19 Having read this text, why do you think the age of steam
   eventually came to an end?   *(1 mark)*

   _____

   _____

   _____

20 Most of the information on the timeline (at the bottom of pages 108 and 109) is
   already included in the other text on these pages.

   Why has the timeline been included?   *(2 marks)*

   _____

   _____

   _____

   _____

   _____

21 Why do you think the author has used the two connected passages
   From Rocket ... to Bullet?   *(1 mark)*

   _____

   _____

   _____

Section 5

These questions are about the text "Travelling in Style" on page 110.

22 The Orient Express has many luxuries. According to the text, where can these luxuries be found on the train? The first one has been done for you.   *(2 marks)*   □ Q22

a piano   in the compartments

wood panelling   in the dining car

fine views ———————————————   in the bar

finest crystal glasses   ———→ through the windows

23 Why does the author use the word "snakes" to describe the train's journey across Europe?   *(2 marks)*   □ Q23

_____

_____

_____

24 In the final sentence, which four separate words emphasise the quality of a journey on the Orient Express?   *(2 marks)*   □ Q24

_____   _____   _____   _____

25 If you were a passenger on the Orient Express, who would you ask if you needed anything?   *(1 mark)*   □ Q25

_____

_____

_____

subtotal

Section 6

These questions are about the whole of the Set A Reading Material.

26 Do you think children today have as much fascination with trains as the three children in *The Railway Children*?

Explain your opinion. *(2 marks)*

_____

_____

_____

_____

27 Why do you think the article "Travelling in Style" has been included at the end of the Reading Material? *(2 marks)*

_____

_____

_____

_____

28 The title of the Reading Material is "On Track". For what reason do you think this title was chosen? *(2 marks)*

_____

_____

29 The text "An Interview With the Railway Children" is adapted from a website all about the film, the characters and the trains.

For what reason might such a website exist? *(2 marks)*

_____

_____

_____

_____

_____

30 Why do you think this Reading Material contains information about *The Railway Children* (including a passage from the book) as well as information about trains and rail travel? *(3 marks)*

_____

_____

_____

_____

_____

_____

END OF TEST

Set

B

KEY STAGE 2
Levels 3–5

Reading Test
Paper

English

Polar Explorer

Reading Test Paper

Polar Explorer

Instructions:

- find a quiet place where you can sit down and complete the test paper undisturbed
- make sure you have all the necessary equipment to complete the test paper
- read the questions carefully
- answer all the questions in this test paper
- go through and check your answers when you have finished the test paper

Time:

This test paper is **1 hour** long.

You should ensure you spend **15 minutes** reading through the Reading Material on pages 123–132 before you begin the test. Do not worry if you have not read all the Reading Material in this time, because you can (and should) look at it as many times as you like during the test.

The main written part of the test should take **45 minutes**. There are several question types:

Multiple choice	you put a ring around the correct option
Short answers	requiring only a word or short phrase
Several line answers	these questions require you to write more than a single point
Explanation answers	you are required to write an answer and explain it, often in quite a lot of detail and with evidence from the text
Other answers	you may be required to draw lines connecting related words

Check how your child has done against the Answers and Mark Scheme on pages 302–304.

Page	133	135	137	139	141	143	144	Max. Mark	**Actual Mark**
Score	....	....	....	....	....	....	....	50	....

First name _____

Last name _____

POLAR EXPLORER

Contents

Introduction

The Arctic and Antarctic regions in general, and the North and South Poles in particular, have long intrigued explorers and adventurers.

In the early years of the twentieth century, there were determined efforts to be the first to reach the Poles and even modern explorers find new challenges in these icy wilderness areas.

On the following pages, you are given a flavour of what the polar regions of our planet are like in *Pole to Pole*. There are also articles on three polar explorers, covering the race to the South Pole and more modern polar exploration. Finally, the poem *Explorer* looks at the way a cat might explore a snow-covered garden.

Pole to Pole

The polar regions are the extremely cold areas found to the far north and south of our planet. They are considered to be among the most inhospitable places on Earth and were the last large areas on Earth to be explored.

The Arctic

The northern polar region is known as the Arctic. This is a huge ocean surrounded by land. The North Pole (the most northerly point on Earth) is in this ocean. However, it is possible to get to the North Pole on foot, because a large proportion of the ocean remains frozen all year round.

During the Arctic winter, the sun never rises and during the summer it never sets, although it remains low in the sky and is therefore very weak.

Although people live on the land at the edge of the Arctic Ocean, they do not live at the North Pole because the ice is floating and moving.

The Antarctic

The Antarctic is the southern polar region and the South Pole can be found here. Unlike the North Pole, the South Pole is completely surrounded by land.

As with the Arctic, the sun never rises during an Antarctic winter and remains close to the horizon during the summer. However, throughout the year the Antarctic remains much colder, partly due to the fact that most of the continent is high above sea level and is covered in thousands of metres of ice, rather than just a few metres as in the Arctic.

There are no native inhabitants on the Antarctic land mass, but special international treaties allow scientists from many countries to live there and undertake valuable research. Much of the information we know about the ozone layer and global warming has come from these scientists.

The following table provides a summary of some key facts about the polar regions of our planet.

	Arctic	Antarctic
Situation	Ocean surrounded by continents	Continent surrounded by oceans
Temperature in winter	–10°C to –30°C	–25°C to –70°C
Temperature in summer	0°C	–2°C to –40°C
Ice thickness	1.5 to 9 metres (floating sea ice)	2500 metres (average thickness)
Main animal life	Polar bears Whales Seals	Penguins Whales Seals
Human inhabitants	Inuits on the land surrounding the frozen ocean	Scientists from many countries

Polar Dream

Helen Thayer was born in New Zealand. She has become a world-famous adventurer, author and photographer, telling the stories of her adventures in words and pictures.

In 1988, at the age of 50, Helen decided to walk alone to the magnetic North Pole without the aid of aircraft, dog teams or snow mobiles. She was totally unsupported. She walked and skied, pulling her own 160 pound sled filled with all her supplies. Her only companion was Charlie, a black Canadian Eskimo Husky, who had been a valuable polar bear dog for the Inuit of Resolute Bay in the polar region of Northern Canada. Charlie's only job was to walk at Helen's side to protect her from polar bears. He did his job well. He saved her life at least once. They were confronted by seven polar bears, one at a time, throughout the almost month-long journey of 586 km (364 miles). Helen circumnavigated the entire magnetic North Pole area.

She began on 30 March and finished on 27 April. It was a long and lonely journey. Helen's expedition was the only one going to the magnetic North Pole in 1988, therefore she had no warning of the ice conditions which lay ahead of her.

She then wrote a book about her journey to the Pole titled *Polar Dream* with a foreword by Sir Edmund Hillary. It is the story of her faithful dog, Charlie, who travelled at her side during her journey. Charlie went home with Helen and lives with three other dogs, four goats and two donkeys. He runs daily with the Thayers, hikes and climbs mountains. He truly enjoys a life of luxury. As Helen will tell you, "What Charlie wants, Charlie gets."

Roald Amundsen

Roald Amundsen, a Norwegian, spent almost all his adult life in exploration. He was the first explorer to navigate the Northwest Passage between the Atlantic and the Pacific oceans to the north of Canada. However, he is most famous for being the first person to reach the South Pole. Yet his journey to Antarctica was almost an accident.

Amundsen was 37 years old when he decided in 1909 to make an attempt on the North Pole, which had not then been reached. But, while he was preparing for the journey, news came that the American explorer Robert Peary had arrived at the Pole. Amundsen secretly changed his plans, telling only his brother, and headed for the South Pole instead. He knew that a British expedition led by Robert Falcon Scott had already set out with the same aim, but travelling by a different route, he overtook the British party. Amundsen's five-man group set out from his base camp in October 1911 on sledges drawn by huskies on what was to be an eight-week journey. On 14 December 1911, Amundsen reached the Pole and planted the Norwegian flag there. He was about four weeks ahead of Scott.

Scott of the Antarctic

Scott of the Antarctic. Who was he?

Scott of the Antarctic is a nickname that has been given to the famous British naval officer and explorer Robert Falcon Scott. From a very early age, however, he was known as "Con" (from the name Falcon). Con joined the navy at the age of 13 and rose through the ranks over the next few years of his life. In late 1911 he led an expedition into unknown areas of Antarctica, aiming to become the first man to stand at the South Pole. On 17 January 1912, Scott reached his destination.

It's cold there. So what do you wear?

Modern polar explorers wear several layers of highly technical thermal, breathable and waterproof clothing. The fabrics used are lightweight and often very expensive. These clothes are used for sleeping too, when the explorer climbs into a specially made sleeping bag. Scott's party had none of this. They had to wear layer on layer of sweaters with woollen hats and woollen and fur mittens. Nature provided them with reindeer fur for boots and sleeping bags.

How on earth do you get to the South Pole?

With great difficulty. Even almost a hundred years later, explorers who attempt to make the South Pole on foot are often thwarted by dangerous conditions, even though they have lightweight equipment and sometimes use teams of dogs to help with the load. Imagine what it must have been like for Scott and his party. They did not have the luxury of a dog team and chose to pull their own supplies across the icy wastes of Antarctica.

So what did Scott find at the South Pole?

The following words were recorded in Scott's diary: "Great God! This is an awful place ..." Unfortunately for Scott it was not just the place itself that was awful. As his team approached the Pole they saw a speck in the distance. They got closer and realised the terrible truth – the speck was a Norwegian flag. Roald Amundsen had beaten them to the South Pole and the tracks of his dogs still lay in the snow. All Scott had to show for the journey were diary entries, photographs and 15 kilograms of fossils collected along the way.

What did Scott do next?

All he could do was turn around and lead his party back home. Luck was not on their side, however. They managed to get themselves just a few miles from relative safety but a huge blizzard and frost-bitten limbs prevented them going further. Scott wrote a final entry in his diary on 29 March, 1912 saying: "The end cannot be far." Somehow, although on the verge of death, he still managed to write letters to his loved ones. The bodies of the party were found eight months later.

Two o'clock:
Let out of the back door of the house, our cat
Is practising the snow.

The layer of white makes a small straight, crumbling cliff
Where we open the back door inwards. The cat
Sniffs at it with suspicion, learns you can just about
Pat at the flaking snow with a careful dab. Then,
A little bolder, he dints it with one whole foot
– And withdraws it, curls it as if slightly lame,

And looks down at it, oddly. The snow is
Different from anything else, not like
A rug, or a stretch of lino, or an armchair to claw upon
And be told to **Get off!**

The snow is peculiar, but not forbidden. The cat
Is welcome to go out in the snow. Does
The snow welcome the cat?
He thinks, looks, tries again.

Three paces out of the door, his white feet find
You sink a little way all of the time, it is slow and cold,
    but it
Doesn't particularly hurt. Perhaps you can even enjoy
    it as something new.
So he walks on, precisely, on the tips of very
    cautious paws …

Half past three, the cat stretched warm indoors,
From the bedroom window we can see his explorations

– From door to fence, from fence to gate, from gate to
    wall to tree, and back,
Are long patterned tracks and trade-routes of round
    paw-marks
Which fresh snow is quietly filling.

By Alan Brownjohn

EXPLORER

Section 1

These questions are about the text "Polar Dream" on page 128.

Choose the correct word or group of words and put a ring around your choice.

1   Helen Thayer travelled to the magnetic North Pole by: *(1 mark)*   ☐
                                                                            Q1

    aircraft.

    snow mobile.

    walking and skiing.

    car.

2   Charlie was a husky dog taken along on the journey to: *(1 mark)*   ☐
                                                                            Q2

    pull the sled.

    scare away polar bears.

    enjoy the walk.

    be nice.

3   After the expedition Charlie: *(1 mark)*   ☐
                                                                            Q3

    went back to the Inuits.

    hunted for polar bears.

    went to live with Helen.

    stayed in the Arctic.

subtotal

4   Helen took a sled along with her to: (1 mark)

    sit on.

    carry her supplies.

    carry rocks she found.

    shelter beneath.

5   Helen wrote a book about her journey called: (1 mark)

    Polar Dream.

    Travel with Charlie.

    My Journey.

    My Autobiography.

6   How did Charlie prove to be an invaluable companion on Helen Thayer's journey?

                                                                 (1 mark)

_____

_____

7 Why does the text tell us that *"What Charlie wants, Charlie gets"*?   *(1 mark)*

_____

_____

_____

8 List three things that made Helen's journey all the more remarkable.   *(2 marks)*

a) _____

b) _____

c) _____

9 Sir Edmund Hillary was the first man to conquer Mount Everest. Why do
   you think the author mentions the fact that Sir Edmund Hillary wrote the
   foreword to Helen's book?   *(1 mark)*

_____

_____

10 Why was Helen Thayer at a disadvantage as the only explorer to the
   magnetic North Pole that year?   *(1 mark)*

_____

_____

_____

subtotal

Section 2

These questions are about the text "Roald Amundsen" on page 129.

11 What caused Amundsen to head for the South Pole?   *(1 mark)*

_____

_____

_____

12 Why do you think Amundsen's plans were kept secret?   *(1 mark)*

_____

_____

_____

13 Give two possible reasons why Amundsen chose a different
route to Scott.   *(2 marks)*

_____

_____

_____

_____

14 Roald Amundsen's achievement was greater than that of Scott or Helen Thayer.

Do you agree with this opinion?
Explain your own opinion fully, using the texts to help you. *(3 marks)*

Q14

_____

_____

_____

_____

_____

_____

subtotal

Section 3

These questions are about the text "Scott of the Antarctic" on page 131.

15 Give two possible reasons, supported by information from the text, for Scott taking longer than Amundsen to reach the Pole.   *(2 marks)*

a) _____

_____

_____

b) _____

_____

_____

16 What in the text indicates that Scott probably expected to die?   *(1 mark)*

_____

_____

17 Why do you think that Scott declared of the Pole, *"Great God! This is an awful place"*?   *(2 marks)*

_____

_____

_____

_____

18 Several items are mentioned in the text about Captain Scott.
Match each item with its purpose. *(2 marks)*

Q18

One has been done for you.

reindeer fur	evidence of expedition
diary	to transport supplies
fossils	to help with research
sledges	sleeping bags
photographs	to record thoughts and feelings

19 Page 131 is clearly divided into questions and answers.

How does this layout help the reader? *(1 mark)*

Q19

_____

_____

_____

subtotal

Section 4

These questions are about the poem "Explorer" by Alan Brownjohn on page 132.

20 What is the cat doing when it is "practising" the snow?   *(1 mark)*

_____

_____

_____

21 In the third verse, the snow is described as *"different from anything else"*.
   What makes it different for the cat?   *(2 marks)*

_____

_____

_____

_____

_____

22 Why does the author describe the snow as *"slow and cold"*?   *(2 marks)*

_____

_____

_____

_____

23 *"From door to fence, from fence to gate, from gate to wall to tree, and back."*
    Why do you think the poet divides this line into short sections
    separated by commas?   *(2 marks)*

Q23

_____

_____

_____

_____

24 Explain what the difference is between the snow in the garden at
    two o'clock and the snow at half past three.   *(2 marks)*

Q24

_____

_____

_____

_____

_____

subtotal

Section 5

These questions are about the whole of the Set B Reading Material.

25 Give two reasons why a trip to the South Pole during its winter
would be more difficult. *(2 marks)*

a) _____

_____

b) _____

_____

26 What purpose is served by the table at the end of the article "Pole to Pole"?
(1 mark)

_____

_____

27 Explain why you think that explorers such as Amundsen, Scott and Helen Thayer
have always had a fascination with the North and South Poles. *(3 marks)*

_____

_____

_____

_____

_____

28 Making reference to the text, consider one advantage and two
disadvantages of a trip to each pole as opposed to the other. *(3 marks)*

Q28

	Advantage	Disadvantage
North Pole	warmer climate	
South Pole		

29 Both texts *Roald Amundsen* and *Scott of the Antarctic* provide information about the
race to be the first explorer to reach the South Pole in the early twentieth century.

Why do you think the following articles have been included? *(3 marks)*

Q29

"Pole to Pole"

_____

_____

_____

"Polar Dream"

_____

_____

_____

subtotal

"Explorer" poem

_____

_____

_____

30 What comparisons can be made between a polar explorer and the cat in
the poem *Explorer*?

Explain your response, making reference to the text if this helps.   *(3 marks)*

_____

_____

_____

_____

_____

_____

END OF TEST

Paper 1: short answer questions

- Your **grammar**, **vocabulary** and **punctuation** will be tested in this task.

- You will be given 45 minutes to complete this task.

1   Insert the capital letters and full stops in the passage below.

the school was closed because of the snow the children didn't mind the

teachers worked at home but the children played in the snow

1 mark

2   Which pair of pronouns is best to complete the sentence below?

The dog chased _____ down the road. _____ ran very fast because we were scared.

Tick **one**.

I	She	☐
her	He	☐
us	We	☐
them	They	☐

1 mark

3   Circle all the **nouns** in the sentence below.

The sun shone through the trees onto the car.

1 mark

4   Circle the **preposition** in the sentence below.

The hurdler jumped over the hurdles.

1 mark

5 Which sentence uses commas correctly?

Tick **one**.

Before, the end of the game the opposition left the pitch. ☐

Before the end of the game, the opposition left the pitch. ☐

Before the end of the game the opposition, left the pitch. ☐

Before the, end of the game, the opposition, left the pitch. ☐ **1 mark**

6 Draw lines to match the words with their most likely final punctuation.

Use each punctuation mark **once**.

Sentence	Punctuation
Help	.
Where is your house	?
I had toast for breakfast	!

1 mark

7 Change the question in the table below into a command.

Write the command in the box.

Question	Command
Can you stop and listen to me?	

1 mark

8 Tick one box to show where the missing **question mark** should go.

Chris asked, "How many days until my birthday" as he looked at the calendar.

☐   ☐   ☐   ☐

1 mark

9 Which of the sentences below uses **commas** correctly?

Tick **one**.

We need a cardboard, tube, glue paper and stick-on eyes. ☐

We need, a cardboard tube glue paper and stick-on eyes. ☐

We need a cardboard tube, glue, paper and stick-on eyes. ☐

We, need a cardboard tube, glue, paper and stick-on eyes. ☐ **1 mark**

10 I helped the <u>pretty</u> little <u>girl</u> to play on the <u>swings</u>.

Put a tick in each row to show whether each underlined word is a **noun** or an **adjective**.

	Noun	Adjective
pretty		
girl		
swings		

1 mark

11 Complete the sentence below with a **contraction** that makes sense.

If you tell us what to buy _____ go shopping for you! **1 mark**

12 Put a tick in each row to show whether the sentence is a statement, a command or a question.

	Statement	Command	Question
Wash the dishes!			
Where is the sink?			
The dishes are dirty.			

1 mark

13 Which sentence contains **two** verbs?

Tick **one**.

Jacob packed his bag and ran to school. ☐

Tiegan ran happily and joyously to school. ☐

Jasmin packed her bag with toys and games. ☐

The phone rang in the hallway. ☐

1 mark

14 Find **one** word that can complete **both** sentences below.

Write the word in the box.

The dog let out a _____ when it saw the cat.

The girl took a rubbing from the _____ of the tree.

```
┌─────────────────────────────────┐
│                                 │
│                                 │
└─────────────────────────────────┘
```

1 mark

15 Complete the sentences below using either **I** or **me**.

____ went to the shops.

Fred and ____ played a board game.

He came with ____ to talk to my teacher.

Why doesn't anyone listen to ____ when I speak?

I had to put my hand up before the teacher would help ____ .

1 mark

16 Which two sentences below should end with a **full stop**?

Tick **two**.

Help, call the police ☐

I like horse riding because it is fun ☐

Do I have to go to the shops with you ☐

Computers make it quicker to produce long texts ☐

1 mark

17 Circle all the **adverbs** in the sentence below.

The mouse scuttled quickly and silently across the floor.

1 mark

18 Put a tick in each row to show whether the sentence is simple, compound or complex.

	simple	compound	complex
My friend is nice.			
My friend, who is called Sarah, is nice.			
My friend is nice and she likes horses.			

2 marks

19 Circle the **connective** in the sentence below.

Despite the bad weather, the Summer Fair raised a lot of

money for new sports equipment.

1 mark

20 Which two of these sentences are **statements**?

Tick **two**.

How long until playtime? ☐

Playtime lasts for 15 minutes. ☐

Go out to play now! ☐

Playtime is in the morning. ☐

Is there a playtime in the afternoon? ☐

1 mark

21 Write a **contraction** to replace the underlined words in each sentence below.

a) We are going on holiday in the summer.

_____ going on holiday in the summer.

b) They have not got any books left in the shop.

They _____ got any books left in the shop.

2 marks

22 Put the teacher's words into direct speech.

The teacher told the children to put their coats on and go out to play.

_____

_____

1 mark

23 Write **two adjectives** to complete the sentence below.

The _____ dog bit the leg of the _____ man. **2 marks**

24 You are looking over your work and decide to replace the word '**lovely**' in the sentence below.

The princess looked lovely in her dress.

Choose another word with a similar meaning and write it in the box.

```



```

1 mark

25 The word **book** has more than one meaning.

Write two sentences to show two **different** meanings.

1) _____

_____

2) _____

_____ **1 mark**

26 Underline the subordinate clause in each sentence below.

After the race had finished, the two drivers shook hands.

The children filed into the classroom because the bell had rung.

Although they were tired, the children kept running. **1 mark**

27 Tick the words that mean the **opposite** of: beautiful.

Tick **one**.

pretty, lovely ☐

unattractive, unsightly ☐

difficult, hard ☐

plentiful, bountiful ☐   **1 mark**

28 A prefix is a letter or a group of letters added to the beginning of a word to make a new word.

For example: **re**cycle

Put a prefix at the beginning of each word to make it mean the opposite.

_____active

_____attractive

_____helpful   **1 mark**

29 Draw lines to match each sentence with the most likely final punctuation.

Sentence	**Punctuation**

Call an ambulance	!
What's your name	.
My birthday is in May	?

1 mark

30 Which ending would make this word an **adverb**?

Soft

Tick **one**.

softness ☐

softs ☐

softly ☐

softer ☐   1 mark

31 Which sentence uses a colon correctly?

Tick **one**.

The note: said jam, butter, cream and scones. ☐

The note said: jam: butter: cream and scones. ☐

The note said: jam, butter, cream and scones. ☐

The note said: jam, butter, cream: and scones. ☐   1 mark

32 Complete the sentences below using either '**were**' or '**was**'.

The cows _____ lying in the field.

Daisy _____ playing in her cot.

The envelope _____ put on the table.

It _____ time to leave for school.   1 mark

33 Write the correct plural form in each space below.

One has been done for you.

one duck, three _____ducks_____

one leaf, three _____

one box, four _____

one child, a group of _____   **1 mark**

34 Look at the passage below. Change all the verbs to the right tense.

One has been done for you.

Yesterday the newspaper <u>is reporting</u> the results from last weekend.

> reported

The children went on a visit yesterday and they <u>will buy</u> some souvenirs.

Eliza is running to the bus stop and she will <u>have been</u> to school.

     1 mark

35 Put a tick to show whether the apostrophe in each sentence is used for
omission or **possession**.

	Apostrophe for omission	Apostrophe for possession
Sam's bike was lying on the ground.		
You're all stars!		
It was Ryan's turn next.		

     1 mark

36 Put one letter in each box to show the **word class**.

Verb	Adjective	Noun	Adverb
A	B	C	D

The loudest lion was obviously the smallest!

☐ ☐ ☐ ☐

1 mark

37 Write this sentence using **Standard English**.

I don't want no help.

_____

1 mark

38 Write this sentence in an **informal** way.

Would you wish to attend a celebration at my house?

_____

1 mark

39 Which of the sentences below is punctuated correctly?

Tick **one**.

Natasha (my best friend) came to my house for a sleepover. ☐

Natasha my (best friend) came to my house for a sleepover. ☐

(Natasha my best friend) came to my house for a sleepover. ☐

Natasha (my best friend came to my house) for a sleepover. ☐   **1 mark**

40 Draw lines to match each word with its homophone.

ate		wait

weight		sale

sail		eight

1 mark

41 Circle the **article** in each sentence below.

Before the concert they all worked hard.

We went on a noisy, scary ride.

I had to put up an umbrella when it was raining.

1 mark

42 Write a sentence that ends with an **ellipsis** to build suspense for your reader.

_____

1 mark

43 Tick one word to complete the sentence below.

The parents and children listened _____ the head teacher welcomed them.

Tick **one**.

between ☐

while ☐

as well as ☐

during ☐

1 mark

44 The sentences below each have an error. The errors are underlined.

Write the correction in the box, making sure that the verb matches the subject.

Our school produces great results. We <u>is</u> proud of ourselves.

Ryan <u>are</u> playing in the park.

1 mark

45 Write a short question beginning with the words below.

How often _____

1 mark

46 Put a tick in each row to show whether the underlined part of the sentence is a **phrase** or a **clause**.

	Phrase	Clause
The old lady crossed the road.		
They had fun playing in the park.		
The children ran **so they could stretch their legs.**		
The snake slithered **in his humid tank.**		

2 marks

A

Levels 3–5

Paper 2: spelling

- Your **spelling** will be tested in this task.

- There are 20 spellings and you will hear each spelling 3 times.

- This section should take approximately 15 minutes to complete, although you will be allowed as much time as you need.

N.B: The answer lines only are given below. You will need to ask someone to read the instructions and sentences to you. These can be found on page 311.

---

1   I am learning to play the _flute_ . ✓

2   We were _traveling_ on the train. — Travelling .

3   The _babies_ were playing on the carpet. ✓

4   The snake _hisses_ loudly in his tank. ✓

5   The explosion caused great _destruction_ . ✓

6   The cow gave birth to two _calves_ . ✓

7   Sam mixed _flour_ into his cake mixture. ✓

8   Max chose to _interfer_ with Tom's game. Interfere

9   Freya's favourite animal was the _elefant_ at the zoo. elephant

10 The man had a very successful _bussiness_ in the city. ✓

11 We watched the film at the _cimiea_ . Cinema

12 The children _hurried_ out to play. ✓

13 Howard Carter was proud to _discover_ the tomb. ✓

14 The children responded to the _critisism_ by improving their work. Criticism

15 Superman was _actually_ Clark Kent. ✓

16 The word love is an _abstract_ noun. ✓

17 Matilda won the _hoping_ race on sports day. hopping   ¹³/₂₀

18 The children were learning about _geometry_ in maths. ✓

19 Mark ran quickly up the _stairs_ . ✓

20 The _parlement_ building is in London. Parliament

Paper 1: short answer questions

- Your **grammar**, **vocabulary** and **punctuation** will be tested in this task.

- You will be given 45 minutes to complete this task.

1 Find **one** word that can complete **both** sentences below.

Write the word in the box.

I needed to _____ my laces as they had come undone.

The man put his _____ around his neck.

```
┌──────────────────────────────────┐
│                                  │
│                                  │
│                                  │
│                                  │
└──────────────────────────────────┘
```

_____
1 mark

2 I ran <u>happily</u> through the <u>scary</u> woods.

Put a tick in each row to show whether each underlined word is an adverb or an adjective.

	Adverb	**Adjective**
happily		
scary		

_____
1 mark

3 Which of these should be written as two separate **sentences**?

Tick **one**.

My rabbit is called Flopsy and my guinea pig is called Jenny. ☐

I am good at writing, but I am better at maths. ☐

Mrs James is my teacher she makes learning fun. ☐

I like horse riding because it is exciting! ☐

_____
1 mark

4   Circle the **preposition** in the sentence below.

The children had to trudge through the mud.

1 mark

5   Write a **question** beginning with the words below.

Why do

1 mark

6   Which two of these sentences are **statements**?

Tick **one**.

How many toys do you have?   ☐

I have 15 different toys.   ☐

Don't show off.   ☐

Do you have a favourite toy?   ☐

My favourite toy is my Batman one.   ☐

1 mark

7   Which of the sentences below is punctuated correctly?

Tick **one**.

Ring me at home (you have my number) so we can chat.   ☐

Ring me (at home you have my number) so we can chat.   ☐

Ring me at home you have my number (so we can chat).   ☐

(Ring me) at home you have my number so we can chat.   ☐

1 mark

8   Draw lines to match each sentence with the most likely final punctuation.

Sentence   **Punctuation**

| How old are you |

| Good gracious |

| I am eight years old |

| ! |

| . |

| ? |

1 mark

9   Look at this sentence:

Stop! You are breaking the law.

What is the name of the punctuation mark that is used after the word '**stop**'?

_____   1 mark

10 Look at this sentence:

The list said he would need gloves, hat, scarf and a warm coat.

a) What is the name of the punctuation mark that is used after the words
    'gloves' and 'hat' in the sentence above?

| |
| |

b) Why is this punctuation mark needed in that sentence?

Tick **one**.

To separate words in a sentence   ☐

To separate the items in a list   ☐

To take the place of full stops   ☐

To mark the start of a new clause   ☐   **2 marks**

11 Change the question in the table below into a command.

Question	Command
Please can you tidy your room?	

1 mark

12 Put a tick in each row to show whether the word is a noun or a verb.

One has been done for you.

	Noun	Verb
tree	✓	
to skip		
hoped		
house		

2 marks

13 Circle the **superlative adjective** in this sentence.

The larger dog yapped at the legs of the smallest dog.

1 mark

14 Put a tick in each row to show whether the sentence is a statement, a command or a question.

	Statement	Command	Question
Can you listen please			
I am listening to the teacher			
Stop and listen			

1 mark

15 Put a tick in each row to show whether the sentence is simple, compound or complex.

	simple	compound	complex
I like spaghetti and I like beans.			
My dinner, which is spaghetti, is tasty.			
My dinner is tasty.			

_____
2 marks

16 Look at the passage below. Change all the verbs from the **past** tense to the **present** tense.

I jumped out of bed and ran to the bathroom.

| | | |

I reversed out of the drive and into a ditch!

| |

Lily had tripped over a large boulder.

| |

_____
2 marks

17 Write a **connective** from the boxes in each space to complete the sentence.

Use each word once.

and	however	because

The children were moaning _____ they did not agree with wearing school

uniform. Jake, _____ , said that he did like wearing uniform

_____ disliked weekends when he had to choose his clothes.

_____
1 mark

18 Tick **one** word to complete the sentence below so that it is grammatically correct.

The house was _____ by the builders.

Tick **one**.

builded ☐

built ☐

build ☐

billed ☐

1 mark

19 Complete the sentences below using either **I** or **me**.

I asked my brother to stop bothering _____ .

Before the end of the day, the teacher told _____ that I had worked hard.

It was time that _____ told the truth about what had happened.

1 mark

20 Insert the missing **inverted commas** in the sentence below.

When you are in a library, said the librarian, you must be silent.

1 mark

21 Which pair of pronouns is best to complete the sentence below?

_____ needed to go to the shops for my mum as _____ had broken her leg.

Tick **one**.

I	she	☐
her	He	☐
We	us	☐
them	They	☐

1 mark

22 Circle the word that describes **how** Freya performed in the competition.

Freya swam amazingly in the competition.   1 mark

23 Which sentence contains **two** verbs?

Tick **one**.

Sam hugged his sister gently.   ☐

The computer whirred noisily on the desk.   ☐

The child jumped and screamed in anger.   ☐

Maisie skipped joyfully to school.   ☐   1 mark

24 Put a tick in each row to show whether the **main** clause or the **subordinate** clause is in bold.

	Main clause	Subordinate clause
The animals stayed inside **because it was snowing outside.**		
The baby, **who was screaming loudly**, would not go to sleep.		
Before school started, **I went to the gym to do some exercise**.		
I cleaned up my bedroom, after my mum had asked me to.		

1 mark

25 Write a **contraction** to replace the underlined words in each sentence below.

a) They are going skiing in the winter.

_____ going skiing in the winter.

b) We will not be able to go to the party.

We _____ be able to go to the party.   2 marks

26 Which of the sentences below uses **question marks** correctly?

Tick **one**.

"How much further do I have to cycle," moaned Tamzin? ☐

"How much further? Do I have to cycle" moaned Tamzin. ☐

"How much further do I have to cycle." moaned Tamzin? ☐

"How much further do I have to cycle?" moaned Tamzin. ☐   1 mark

27 You are looking over your work and decide to replace the word '**looked**' in the sentence below.

"Land ahoy!" shouted the captain as he looked out to sea.

Choose a suitable word and write it in the box.

```
┌─────────────────────────────────┐
│                                 │
│                                 │
└─────────────────────────────────┘
```
1 mark

28 The word **ring** has more than one meaning.

Write two sentences to show two **different** meanings.

1) _____

_____

2) _____

_____   1 mark

29 Draw lines to match each word with its homophone.

mail		whole

hole		male

bear		bare

1 mark

30 Tick the words that mean the **opposite** of: tough.

Tick **one**.

rough, hard ☐

mean, aggressive ☐

strong, hardy ☐

fragile, delicate ☐

1 mark

31 Put one letter in each box to show the **word class**.

Verb	Adjective	Noun	Adverb
A	B	C	D

The helpful child was talking loudly!
☐ ☐ ☐   ☐

1 mark

32 A prefix is a letter or a group of letters added to the beginning of a word to make a new word.

For example: **im**possible

Put a prefix at the beginning of each word to make it mean the opposite.

_____easy

_____mature

_____agree

1 mark

33 Put a tick to show whether the apostrophe in each sentence is used for **omission** or **possession**.

	Apostrophe for omission	Apostrophe for possession
You'll need to work hard today!		
I won't be able to help you.		
Claire's work is the best!		

1 mark

34 Write this sentence using **commas** in the correct places.

The children who were all aged 4 went on a visit to the zoo.

_____

_____

1 mark

35 Write a different **adverb** in each space below to help describe what Matilda did.

Matilda wrote _____ and finished her story _____ .

2 marks

36 Add a **suffix** to this word to make an **adjective**.

friend_____

1 mark

37 Look at this sentence:

Jack and Jill went up the hill…came tumbling after.

What is the name of the punctuation mark that is used after the word
'**hill**' in the sentence?

_____

1 mark

38 Write this sentence using correct punctuation.

One has been done for you.

W
when i wake up in the morning i have to have a shower after that
i have my breakfast

_____

_____

1 mark

39 Which sentence uses the correct **plural**?

Tick **one**.

The baby were all looking sweet in their prams. ☐

The man all lined up at the start of the race. ☐

The child played together in the park. ☐

The tomatoes ripened in the sun. ☐

1 mark

40 Complete the sentences below using either 'is' or 'are'.

The child _____ sitting on the fence.

The children _____ sitting on the fence.

The geese _____ flying in the sky.

The animals _____ lined up at the show.

1 mark

41 Complete the sentence below with a **contraction** that makes sense.

I am sorry but I _____ be able to come to your party.

1 mark

42 Write this sentence using **Standard English**.

I should of done my homework last night.

_____

1 mark

43 Write this sentence in an informal way.

It was awfully generous of you to give me a birthday gift.

_____

1 mark

44 Circle the **article** in each sentence below.

The window was mended at last.

It was an unfortunate mistake.

I saw a lion when I was on holiday.

1 mark

45 Write this sentence correctly, using correct punctuation.

My mum asked me to buy lettuce bread tomatoes and cheese.

_____

_____ **1 mark**

46 Put a tick in each row to show whether the underlined part of the sentence is a **phrase** or a **clause**.

	Phrase	Clause
The news spread quickly on the radio.		
The noisy children **played in the park**.		
To get away from the lion, **the animals stampeded**.		
The baby screamed **in the wooden cot**.		

2 marks

Paper 2: spelling

- Your **spelling** will be tested in this task.

- There are 20 spellings and you will hear each spelling 3 times.

- This section should take approximately 15 minutes to complete, although you will be allowed as much time as you need.

N.B: The answer lines only are given below. You will need to ask someone to read the instructions and sentences to you. These can be found on pages 311–312.

1 The _____ pumps blood around the body.

2 The hare is _____ than the tortoise.

3 Sir Lancelot was a brave _____ .

4 The fisherman _____ the size of the fish he caught.

5 The elephant is a large _____ .

6 My aunt made green tomato _____ to have with cheese.

7 Magicians will not _____ their secrets.

8 To read a map successfully, you need to know what the _____ mean.

9 Two _____ make a whole.

10 The bride and groom _____ in a church.

11 A _____ is a 3D shape.

12 Matthew's car stopped _____ .

13 Ian was proud of the _____ he had grown.

14 Wallace and Gromit is a funny _____ .

15 The children _____ talking when the teacher entered the room.

16 There are one thousand metres in a _____ .

17 The athlete _____ the world record in the 100m sprint.

18 The bride walked down the _____ in her beautiful white dress.

19 The children went _____ for a school visit.

20 The baby _____ started to cry when she was put to bed.

Paper 1: short answer questions

- Your **grammar**, **vocabulary** and **punctuation** will be tested in this task.

- You will be given 45 minutes to complete this task.

1   Circle all the **adjectives** in the sentence below.

The kind dog helped the old lady over the uneven ground.

1 mark

2   josh is travelling to london on the train to visit samuel.

   a) Circle the three words in the sentence above that should start with a capital letter.

   b) For one of the words you have identified, explain why it would need a capital letter.

     Word chosen _____

     _____

     _____

2 marks

3   Complete the sentences below using either **I** or **me**.

Tim and _____ went to the shops.

Finally it was my turn, _____ had to perform to the audience.

My parents were very proud of _____ .

1 mark

4 Insert the missing **question mark** into one of the sentences below.

" Do I have to go to school today " moaned Simon

" Of course you do , you are the headteacher " his wife replied

1 mark

5 Put a tick in each row to show whether the sentence is a statement, a command or a question.

	Statement	Command	Question
I like eating pasta			
Cook the pasta			
Which pasta is your favourite			

1 mark

6 Draw lines to match each word with its homophone.

pear	bare
groan	grown
bear	pair

1 mark

7 Draw lines to match each sentence with the most likely final punctuation.

Sentence   **Punctuation**

Sentence	Punctuation
Where do you live	!
I live in England	.
Help, help, help	?

1 mark

8 Which pair of pronouns is best to complete the sentence below?

It is time for _____ to perform _____ musical piece.

Tick **one**.

I	she	☐
her	He	☐
her	her	☐
them	They	☐

1 mark

9 Circle all the **adverbs** in the sentences below.

Mournfully, Zac trudged to boring school. He angrily kicked a rusty can that was on the pavement.

1 mark

10 Complete the sentences below using either '**run**' or '**ran**'.

I can _____ fast.

The child _____ to school.

Jake _____ as fast as he was able to.

The children _____ quickly during the race last week.

2 marks

11 Which of the sentences below is punctuated correctly?

Tick **one**.

We packed lots of things (including the map) for our journey. ☐

We packed (lots of things including the map) for our journey. ☐

We packed lots of things including the map (for our journey). ☐

(We packed lots of things) including the map for our journey. ☐

1 mark

12 I <u>shouted</u> <u>loudly</u> because I <u>was</u> lost.

Put a tick in each row to show whether each underlined word is an adverb or a verb.

	Verb	**Adverb**
shouted		
loudly		
was		

1 mark

13 Write a sentence that needs to end with an **exclamation mark**.

_____

1 mark

14 Circle the most suitable **connective** to complete the sentence below.

The children ran for shelter _____ it started to rain.

although		because		yet		finally

1 mark

15 Circle the **two verbs** in the sentence below.

The colourful ball broke the window as it flew through the air.

1 mark

16 Look at the passage below. Change all the verbs from the **present** tense to the **future** tense.

I am running to school so that I am early.

George is training hard.

The cows jump over the moon!

2 marks

17 Each of the sentences below is missing a verb.

Draw a line to match each sentence with the correct verb.

Sentence   **Verb**

The lions _____ eating their dinner.

Brookside School _____ won the cup.

Jason _____ fallen off his bike.

has

have

are

1 mark

18 Which sentence uses commas correctly?

Tick **one**.

Suddenly there was, silence in the stadium. ☐

Suddenly, there was silence in the stadium. ☐

Suddenly there was silence in, the stadium. ☐

Suddenly there, was silence in the stadium. ☐   **1 mark**

19 Circle the correct form of the **verb** in brackets to complete each sentence.

(are / is)

The children _____ noisy!

(ran / run)

Marcus and Lyn _____ quickly to school and arrived on time.

(play / plays)

I _____ games with my little brother.   **2 marks**

20 Put a circle around the words that should have a **capital letter** at the start.

tim, chris and kierton had all been friends since they had been at school.   **1 mark**

21 Put one letter in each box to show the **word class**.

Verb	Adjective	Noun	Adverb
A	B	C	D

We went happily on holiday to sunny Spain.

☐ ☐   ☐ ☐

1 mark

22 Write a sentence that ends with an **ellipsis** to build suspense for your reader.

_____

1 mark

23 Change the question in the table below into a command.

Write the command in the box.

Question	Command
Can you help me make the lunch?	

1 mark

24 Write this sentence in an informal way.

My teacher is terribly strict but very good at teaching as she makes learning enjoyable.

_____

1 mark

25 Which sentence uses **inverted commas** correctly?

"I wish it was the end of school, whined Tom, because I am going to play football." ☐

I wish it was the end of school, "whined Tom, because I am going to play football." ☐

"I wish it was the end of school," whined Tom, "because I am going to play football." ☐

I wish it was the end of school, "whined Tom," because I am going to play football. ☐

1 mark

26 Write this sentence using **Standard English**.

I ain't never going back.

_____

1 mark

27 Tick the words that mean the opposite of: bright

dark, dreary ☐

blazing, brilliant ☐

radiant, polished ☐

vivid, twinkling ☐

1 mark

28 Write the correct plural form in each space below.

One has been done for you.

one chicken, three <u>chickens</u>

one man, four _____ .

one goose, a pair of _____ .

one cow, a herd of _____ .

1 mark

29 Put a tick to show whether the apostrophe in each sentence is used for **omission** or **possession**.

	Apostrophe for omission	Apostrophe for possession
Mya's coat is on the peg.		
Nick's digger is in the sandpit.		
They'll have to tidy up later!		

1 mark

30 Put a tick in each row to show whether the sentence is simple, compound or complex.

	Simple	Compound	Complex
My bike, which goes very fast, is shiny and new.			
My bike is shiny and new.			
My bike is shiny but my helmet is old.			

1 mark

31 Which sentence uses a colon correctly?

Tick **one**.

To make the model I needed: glue, paint and card. ☐

To make the model I needed: glue: paint and card. ☐

To make the model: I needed glue, paint and card. ☐

To make the model: I needed: glue, paint and card. ☐ **1 mark**

32 Write a **contraction** to replace the underlined words in each sentence below.

a) I should not have any more pudding!

I _____ have any more pudding!

b) It will be alright on the night!

_____ be alright on the night! **2 marks**

33 Insert **three** commas in the correct places in the sentence below.

In my school bag I have a maths book a pencil case a coat a plastic frog and a pair of glasses. **1 mark**

34 Add a **suffix** to this word to make an **adjective**.

skill = skil_____ . **1 mark**

35 Circle the **article** in each sentence below.

An ostrich was running around.

The park was closed today.

I wanted a computer for my birthday. **1 mark**

36 Put a tick in each row to show whether the **main** clause or the
subordinate clause is in bold.

	Main clause	Subordinate clause
Finally, **after a long journey**, we had arrived.		
The girl, **who was beautiful**, was dancing to the music.		
During the performance, **the scenery fell down and hit the actors!**		
Oscar, who was scared of heights, **climbed up the telegraph pole**.		

1 mark

37 Which two of these sentences are **statements**?

Tick **two**.

I am very hungry. ☐

Help! I need food! ☐

Why did you not eat breakfast? ☐

How long until lunchtime? ☐

Dinner is my favourite meal of the day. ☐

1 mark

38 Write a sentence containing a pair of **brackets**.

_____

_____

1 mark

39 Write a **question** beginning with the words below.

Who is _____

1 mark

40 Insert the capital letters and full stops in the passage below.

it had been many years since oxford had won the race

they had been working extra hard this year

1 mark

41 The word **watch** has more than one meaning.

Write two sentences to show two **different** meanings.

1) _____

_____

2) _____

_____

1 mark

42 Circle the **preposition** in the sentence below.

The bear was hiding in the cave.

1 mark

43 A prefix is a letter or a group of letters added to the beginning of a word to make a new word.

For example: **dis**advantage

Put a prefix at the beginning of each word to make it mean the opposite.

_____afraid

_____comfort

_____probable

1 mark

44 Complete the sentence below with a **contraction** that makes sense.

I _____ like eating sprouts, even at Christmas!   **1 mark**

45 Put a tick in each row to show whether the underlined part of the sentence is a **phrase** or a **clause**.

	Phrase	**Clause**
The phone beeped **in the silent room**.		
The mouse squeaked in his house.		
The quiet baby **slept in her cot**.		
They went into town **so they could buy some food**.		

2 marks

46 Which word is closest in meaning to '**scoured**' in the sentence below?

They <u>scoured</u> the school for the boy.

Tick **one**.

built ☐

searched ☐

taught ☐

opened ☐   **1 mark**

Paper 2: spelling

- Your **spelling** will be tested in this task.

- There are 20 spellings and you will hear each spelling 3 times.

- This section should take approximately 15 minutes to complete, although you will be allowed as much time as you need.

> **N.B: The answer lines only are given below. You will need to ask someone to read the instructions and sentences to you. These can be found on pages 311–312.**

1 The children used a _____ stick to draw a line.

2 Ali Baba and the forty _____ is a good pantomime.

3 The school _____ welcomed the visitors.

4 A line of _____ were led along the beach.

5 Margaret enjoys ballroom _____ .

6 Jean knitted a green _____ for her grandson.

7 Howard Carter entered the _____ cautiously.

8 The mother bought a _____ pack of crisps.

9 Flying is the _____ way to travel to New York from England.

10 The children were told to _____ their names on their work.

11 Shoes are _____ on the beach.

12 The church service included a _____ .

13 The giraffe has an _____ long neck.

14 Mum _____ Philip's bag home from school.

15 Your birthday _____ on the same date every year.

16 They were _____ to reach the South Pole.

17 Jemima was _____ her pocket money to buy an action figure.

18 Grandpa was _____ wood for the fire.

19 Children _____ from regular exercise.

20 Paul staggered under the _____ of the suitcase.

Paper 1: extended task

- Your **grammar**, **punctuation** and **vocabulary** will be tested in a piece of extended writing.

- The focus for the task should be on the range of sentence structures and punctuation marks you use to control your writing.

- Spelling will not be assessed in this task. Try to use a wide range of ambitious vocabulary in your response.

- **You will have 30 minutes for this task.**

A Sporting Event

You have been asked to write a report about a sporting event that you attended as a spectator. The report should explain what the sport is and what you experienced. The report will be printed in a local newspaper.

It is up to you to choose which sport and, therefore, which event you are reporting on. You can make up any details that you wish, but try to base it on a realistic experience you have had.

Remember to use:

- Appropriate, varied sentence structures

- A broad range of punctuation to control your writing

- Imaginative and precise words to convey your meaning.

You will **not** be marked on spelling.

Your task is to write the report.

A

Paper 2: short answer questions

Level 6

- Your **grammar**, **vocabulary** and **punctuation** will be tested in this task.

- You have 20 minutes to complete this task.

1   Use a connective or connective phrase to complete the sentence below.

_____ the flags were mounted on the flagpoles, there was no wind to make them blow.

1 mark

2   Which of the sentences below uses **semi-colons** correctly?

Tick **one**.

The wind was; very strong the kite flew high in the sky. ☐

The wind was very strong; the kite flew high in the sky. ☐

The wind was very strong, the kite; flew high in the sky. ☐

The wind was very strong, the kite flew; high in the sky. ☐   **1 mark**

3   Put a tick in each row to show the type of **connective** underlined in each sentence.

	Subordinating connective	Coordinating connective
The ducks were hungry, **but** there was no bread.		
Until we heard the final whistle, we worked hard to score a goal.		
Because it was raining, the children played indoors.		
We were late home for dinner, **so** it had been thrown away.		

1 mark

4   Use the prepositions in the boxes to complete the sentences below.

| past | under | at | along |

Use each preposition **once**.

She walked _____ the path.

My dog ran _____ the churchyard.

They'll arrive _____ the correct time.

They drove _____ the railway line.   **1 mark**

5   Expand the noun into a noun phrase by adding words before **and** after the noun.

One has been done for you.

Noun	Noun phrase
the chimney	the brick chimney on top of the roof
the apple	

1 mark

6   Circle the correct form of the verb in each set of brackets.

The trees (sway / sways) gently in the breeze.

The goats (have / has) two horns each.

The children (are / is) too noisy!   **1 mark**

7   Which of the sentences below is punctuated correctly?

Tick **one**.

(The hotel, by the sea) had beautiful views from the windows. ☐

The hotel (by the sea) had beautiful views from the windows. ☐

The hotel (by the sea had beautiful views) from the windows. ☐

The hotel (by the sea had beautiful views from the windows). ☐   **1 mark**

8   Write the **contraction** of each pair of underlined words in the box below it.

It is nearly the holidays, I am so excited!

We cannot attend the party as we are busy.

You are working hard at your learning.

2 marks

9   Match the root word to its meaning.

Root word   **Meaning**

Root word		Meaning
aqua		people
demo		animal
zoo		water

1 mark

10 Put a tick in each row to show which prefix could be added to each root word.

	af-	mal-	dis-	mis-
-align				
-inform				
-nourished				
-appear				
-firm				

2 marks

11 This sentence is in the **active voice**.

The dog ate the bone.

Write it in the **passive voice**:

_____

1 mark

12 This sentence is written in the personal form.

I find it difficult to perform the high jump.

Which sentence below is a correct **impersonal** form of the sentence?

Tick **one**.

I don't like performing the high jump. ☐

The high jump is difficult to perform. ☐

To do the high jump, takes me a lot of effort. ☐

I find it hard to do the high jump. ☐

1 mark

13 Rewrite this sentence in a more **concise** way.

It appears to me, on balance, weighing up all the possibilities, that it might be, although I am not certain, a good idea to bring in a new school uniform because then, I think, the children might like to wear it.

_____

_____ **1 mark**

14 Write the **infinitive form** of each verb listed in the table below.

One has been done for you.

Verb	Infinitive form
dances, danced, dancing	to dance
have, had, has	
running, ran, runs	
flies, flew, flown	

1 mark

15 Which of the sentences below uses **dashes** correctly?

Tick **one**.

Her favourite song Lift Me Up – was playing on the radio. ☐

Her – favourite song – Lift Me Up was playing on the radio. ☐

Her favourite song – Lift Me Up – was playing on the radio. ☐

Her favourite song – Lift Me Up was playing on the radio. ☐ **1 mark**

16 Which **two** things does **impersonal writing** NOT contain?

Tick **two**.

Use of the personal pronoun 'I' ☐

Use of emotive words ☐

Use of evidence to back up a viewpoint ☐

Use of the third person ☐

1 mark

17 The sentence below is written in the active voice.

The dog knocked the vase over.

Which sentence is the **passive** form of the sentence above?

Tick **one**.

The dog, who was called Dribbles, knocked over the vase. ☐

The dog caused the vase to break. ☐

The vase was knocked over by the dog. ☐

Because the dog was excited, he knocked the vase over. ☐

1 mark

18 Write an example of each type of **noun** in the boxes below.

Abstract noun ☐

Collective noun ☐

Common noun ☐

Proper noun ☐

2 marks

A

Level 6

Paper 3: spelling

- Your **spelling** will be tested in this task.

- There are 15 spellings and you will hear each spelling 3 times.

- This section should take approximately 15 minutes to complete, although you will be allowed as much time as you need.

N.B: The answer lines only are given below. You will need to ask someone to read the instructions and sentences to you. These can be found on pages 311–312.

---

1   The teacher said that the children's behaviour was _____ .

2   It took two _____ hours to complete the work.

3   The costumes at Halloween were _____ .

4   The police used _____ analysis to find the suspect.

5   There was a _____ locomotive for the children to ride on.

6   A person who writes stories is a _____ .

7   Sharon put a _____ in the bottle of drink.

8   Year 6 were _____ about going to secondary school.

9   The man helped change the tyre; he was a _____ chap.

10 When the country is surrounded by water, the inhabitants are _____ .

11 The children played a game of _____ .

12 He was a _____ sight, sitting all on his own at the bus stop.

13 Some people are more _____ to being hypnotised than others.

14 It was _____ to try and cycle to school in the hurricane.

15 The country was in _____ after the death of the King.

Set

A

KEY STAGE 2
Levels 3–5

Test Paper 1

Science

Test Paper 1

Test Paper 1

Instructions:

- find a quiet place where you can sit down and complete the test paper undisturbed
- make sure you have all the necessary equipment to complete the test paper
- read the questions carefully
- answer all the questions in this test paper
- go through and check your answers when you have finished the test paper

✎ This pencil shows where you will have to put your answer. Sometimes you may have to draw the answer instead of writing one.

Time:

This test paper is **45 minutes** long.

Note to Parents:

Check how your child has done against the Answers and Mark Scheme on pages 313–314.

Page	197	199	201	203	205	207	209	Max. Mark	**Actual Mark**
Score	....	....	....	....	....	....	....	40	....

First name ....

Last name ....

Different Materials

1 Ali has some blocks made of different materials.

The blocks are all the same size.

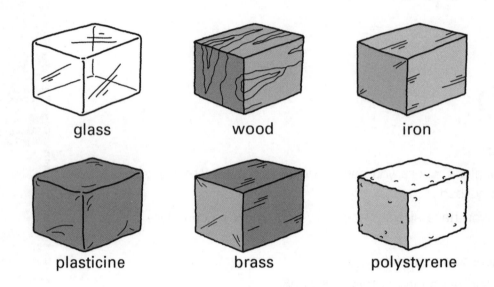

glass   wood   iron

plasticine   brass   polystyrene

a) The glass block is 'transparent'.

What is meant by the word 'transparent'?

Transparent ~~means~~ means you can
see through it _____ (1 mark)

b) **Which block could be made into a magnet?**

Iron can be made into a magnet ___ (1 mark)

c) One block can be easily reshaped.

Which block is this?

✎ The block is plasticine _____ (1 mark)

d) Which two blocks would float in water?

✎ The two blocks that would float in water are
wood

and polystyrene _____ (2 marks)

e) Arrange the three blocks in this list in order of increasing hardness.

iron   polystyrene   wood

✎ least hard   Polystyrene _____

wood _____

hardest   iron _____

(2 marks)

f) i Ali buys some polystyrene tiles and sticks them to the ceiling in the kitchen.

Suggest why Ali might have done this.

Ali might have done this to decorate.

(1 mark)

ii Write down **TWO** properties of polystyrene that make it suitable for this use.

Two properties are to absorb absorb sound and it is light weight.

(2 marks)

(Total 10 marks)

On the Farm

2 Class 4C visit a farm.

The farmer shows the children the plants he grows.

a) Why does the farmer grow lots of plants?

The farmer grows lots of plants to sell (1 mark)

Q2a

b) The children see rabbits eating the farmer's carrots.

The farmer says the fox eats some of the rabbits.

Draw the food chain by writing the words in the boxes.

Choose the words from this list.

carrots   **fox**   **rabbits**

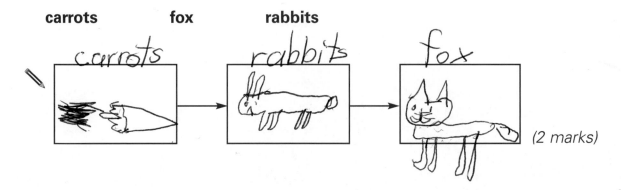

(2 marks)

Q2b

subtotal

c) Put a ring around the part of the food chain that is a predator.

carrots   (fox)   rabbits   (1 mark)

d) The farmer will soon dig up his carrots.

What effect will this have on the rabbits?

The rabbits will be hungry

_____ (1 mark)

(Total 5 marks)

Drying the Washing

3 Kim hangs wet washing on a clothes line.

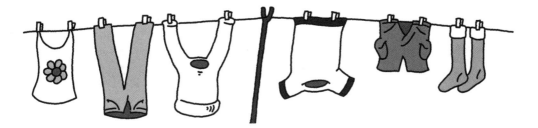

The washing dries without it raining.

a) Write down **TWO** things that will help the washing to dry quickly.

✎ Two things are: the sun and the wind.

_____ *(2 marks)*

Q3a

b) Finish the sentence by using the best word from this list.

boiling   evaporating   freezing   melting

✎ When the clothes dry, the water is *evaporating*   *(1 mark)*

Q3b

c) In the evening the washing is dry. Kim forgets to bring in the washing. Next morning the washing is wet, even though it did not rain in the night. **Suggest the most likely reason for this happening.**

✎ The morning dew made the clothes wet.

_____ *(2 marks)*

Q3c

(Total 5 marks)

subtotal

Strong Magnet

4 Chris has three magnets.

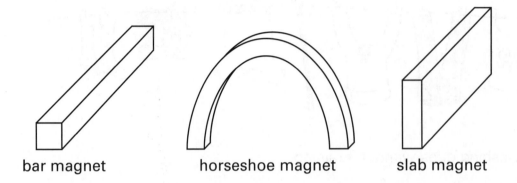

bar magnet   horseshoe magnet   slab magnet

He is trying to find out which is the strongest magnet.

Chris finds out that each magnet can pick up paper clips.

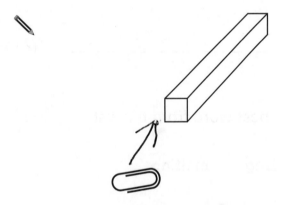

a) Draw an arrow to show the pull of the magnet on the paper clip. *(1 mark)*

b) Chris finds out how many paper clips each magnet can pick up.

Here are his results.

Magnet	Number of paper clips
bar	26
horseshoe	20
slab	35

Finish the bar chart. Draw a bar to show how many paper clips each magnet picked up.

One bar has been done for you.

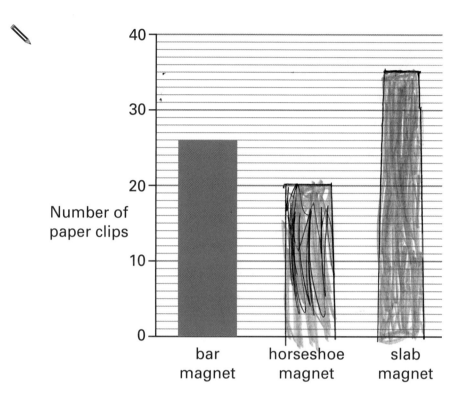

(2 marks)

Q4b

c) Which magnet is the strongest?

The slab magnet _____ (1 mark)

Q4c

d) Chris has many ideas about why this is the strongest magnet.

Tick **ONE** box to show the best idea.

It is the largest. ☐

It is the heaviest. ☑

It picks up the most paper clips. ☐

(1 mark)

Q4d

(*Total 5 marks*)

Pulse Rate

5 Jenny wears a pulse rate meter attached to her ear lobe.

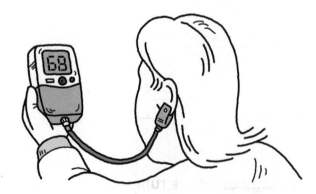

She records her pulse rate at playtime.

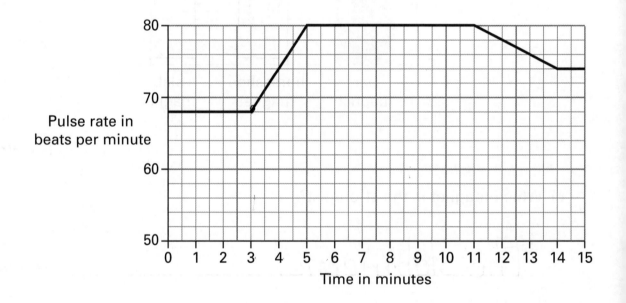

a) What was Jenny's highest pulse rate?

✎ _80_____ beats per minute   *(1 mark)*

b) What was Jenny's pulse rate at 3 minutes?

✎ _60,4_____ beats per minute   *(1 mark)*

c) After 3 minutes Jenny started to run around.

How can you tell this from the graph?

                                    Pulse
I can tell because her ~~heart~~ rate had

~~you~~ gone up. _____ (1 mark)

Q5c

d) Why does Jenny's pulse rate change as she is running?

Jenny's pulse rate has changed because

she using more oxygen and her body is producting

more - oxygen. _____ (2 marks)

Q5d

e) For how many minutes is Jenny running around?

For 10 (ten) _____ minutes   (1 mark)

Q5e

(Total 6 marks)

subtotal

Keeping the Coffee Warm

6 Abdul wants to find out which material will keep his coffee warm.

He makes his coffee from boiled water.

Abdul uses sensors connected to a computer to measure the temperature every 5 minutes.

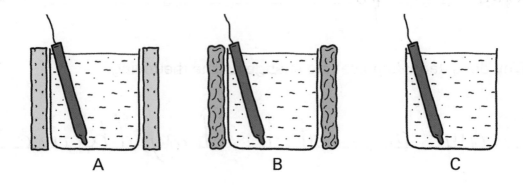

The graph shows his results.

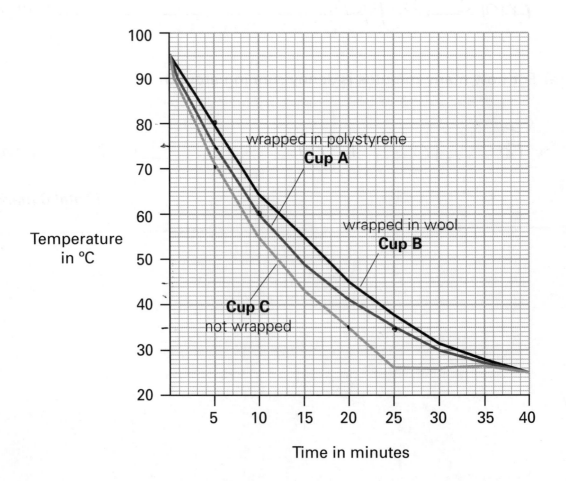

a) What temperature was the coffee in **Cup A** at 25 minutes?

✎ _35_ °C

(1 mark)

Q6a

b) Tick **ONE** box to show in which cup the coffee cooled the fastest.

✎ **Cup A** ☐   **Cup B** ☐   **Cup C** ☑

(1 mark)

Q6b

c) Use the graph. Estimate the temperature of the room.

✎ _25_ °C

(1 mark)

Q6c

d) Complete the sentence. Choose words from this list.

electrical conductor   **thermal insulator**   **thermal conductor**

The material that keeps the coffee warm is a good

✎ _thermal insulator_ _____ *(1 mark)*

Q6d

e) Describe one other way that Abdul could help to stop heat leaving his coffee to keep it warmer for longer.

✎ _One other way is to put the cup on a hot_

surface. _____ *(1 mark)*

Q6e

(Total 5 marks)

subtotal

Mirrors and Light Rays

7 Jamil cycles home from school.

He approaches a sharp bend in the road.

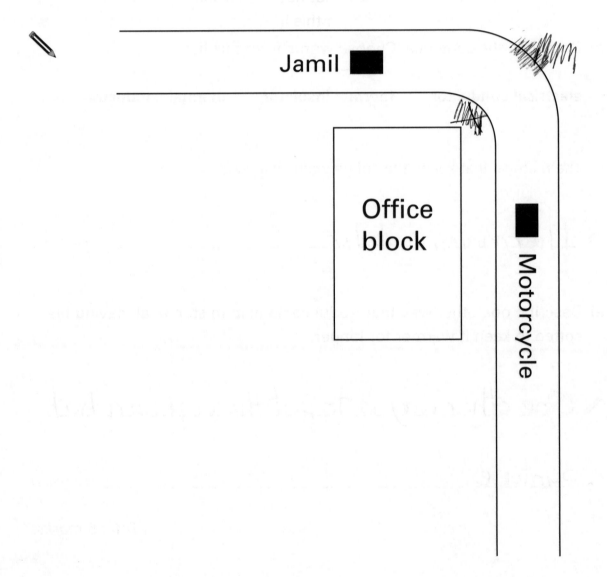

Jamil

Office block

Motorcycle

a) Show, by drawing light rays on the diagram on page 208,
   how a mirror placed at the bend in the road could enable Jamil to
   see the motorcycle. *(2 marks)*

b) Why can he not see the motorcycle coming towards him around the
bend?

He can not see round corners

_____ *(1 mark)*

c) Which word best describes what happens when a light ray hits the
   mirror? Choose the word from this list.

   radiates   **rebounds**   **reflects**

reflects _____ *(1 mark)*

(Total 4 marks)

END OF TEST

Set

A

KEY STAGE 2
Levels 3–5

Test Paper 2

Science

Test Paper 2

Test Paper 2

Instructions:

- find a quiet place where you can sit down and complete the test paper undisturbed
- make sure you have all the necessary equipment to complete the test paper
- read the questions carefully
- answer all the questions in this test paper
- go through and check your answers when you have finished the test paper

✎ This pencil shows where you will have to put your answer. Sometimes you may have to draw the answer instead of writing one.

Time:

This test paper is **45 minutes** long.

Note to Parents:

Check how your child has done against the Answers and Mark Scheme on pages 314–315.

Page	211	213	215	217	219	221	223	225	Max. Mark	**Actual Mark**
Score	....	....	....	....	....	....	....	....	40	....

First name ....

Last name ....

Circuits

1 Emily is setting up an electrical circuit. She has wires, switches, bulbs and cells (batteries). She does not use them all.

a) Draw three lines to match each drawing to its symbol.

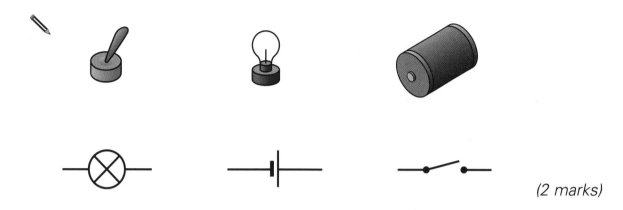

(2 marks)

Look at the picture of Emily's circuit.

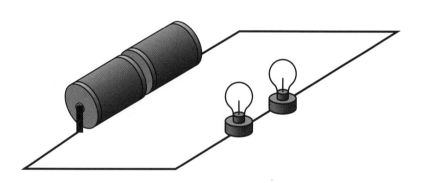

b) Use the symbols to draw a diagram of Emily's circuit.

(1 mark)

The bulbs in Emily's circuit are very bright. Emily removes a cell (battery) from the circuit.

c) **Complete the sentence below to describe the effect on the bulbs of removing a cell.**

The bulbs will be _____ *(1 mark)*

d) **Emily adds some different materials to her circuit.**

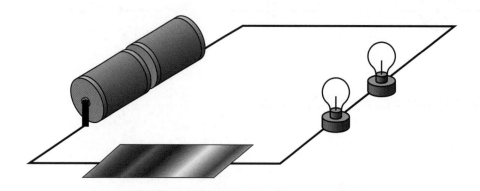

When some materials are placed in the circuit, the bulbs light up. Some materials do not allow the bulbs to light up. This table shows her results.

i **Finish the table by adding TWO ticks to show the results for plastic and iron.**

Material	Bulbs light up	Bulbs do not light up
tin	✓	
plastic		
iron		

(1 mark)

ii Finish these sentences. Choose your words from this list.

conductor   **elastic**   **insulator**

Copper allows electricity to pass through the circuit. Copper is a/an

_____

Wood does not allow electricity to pass through the circuit. Wood is a/an

_____   *(2 marks)*

Q1dii

(Total 7 marks)

subtotal

Earth, Sun and Moon

2 Jane and Becky are talking to Class 6B about the Earth, the Sun and the Moon. They are using models (a football, a pea and a small bead) to represent the Earth, the Sun and the Moon.

a) Draw three lines to match each model to what it represents.

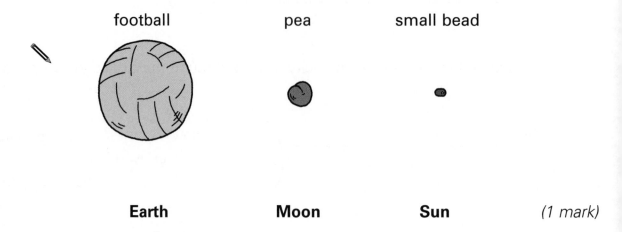

football   pea   small bead

Earth   **Moon**   **Sun**   *(1 mark)*

b) Jane will show how the Earth orbits the Sun. Becky is pretending to be the Sun and stands in the middle of the room.

Draw the path Jane should walk around Becky to show the Earth's orbit.

Becky

Jane

(1 mark)

c) Jane has some ideas about the Earth, the Sun and the Moon.

Write **true** or **false** below each idea.

(2 marks)

Q2c

(Total 4 marks)

Experiments with Evaporating

3 Sue and Sam are carrying out an experiment to see how fast evaporation takes place. They are going to measure out some water and leave it in a shallow dish. Every day they are going to measure the volume of water that remains.

Here is a table of their results.

	Start	Day 1	Day 2	Day 3	Day 4	Day 5
Volume of water in cm³	50	34	25	18	9	0

subtotal

a) Finish the bar chart to show their results at day 2, day 3, day 4 and day 5.

Volume of water in cm³

(2 marks)

b) After how many days has half the water evaporated?

✎ _____ *(1 mark)*

c) Different liquids evaporate at different rates under the same conditions.
   Put the three liquids in this list in order of how quickly they evaporate.
   Put the liquid that evaporates fastest first.

   motor oil   petrol   water

   ✎ evaporates fastest   _____

                               _____

   evaporates slowest   _____   *(2 marks)*

(Total 5 marks)

Plants

4   Tim grows lots of plants. Some of the plants are for Tim to eat.

a) Circle the **TWO** that Tim would be most likely to eat.

        grass   apple   lettuce   daffodil   *(2 marks)*

Q4a

Some of the plants are grown in pots.

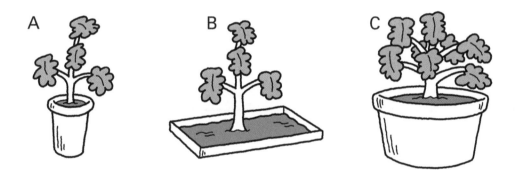

b) Explain why **Plant A** and **Plant B** are not growing as well as **Plant C**.

_____

_____ *(2 marks)*

Q4b

subtotal

c) Tim's mum put some plants in the garden. One plant was left in a dark cupboard.

Plants in garden   **Plant left in cupboard**

i Describe **TWO** things that are different about the plant left in the cupboard.

✎ _____

_____ *(2 marks)*

ii What caused the plant in the cupboard to grow like this?

✎ _____ *(1 mark)*

(Total 7 marks)

Soil

5 Alan is making a new garden at his house. He looks at the soil and finds that there are many small pebbles in the soil. He needs to remove the pebbles before he can sow grass for a lawn.

a) **What piece of equipment does he use to remove pebbles from the soil?**

_____ *(1 mark)*

Q5a

b) He takes samples from two different places in the garden. He puts each sample of soil into a funnel and adds water.

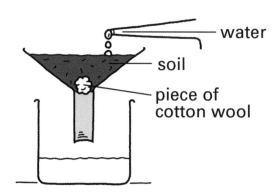

He times how long it takes for the water to pass through the soil into the beaker.

Write down two things that he should do to ensure this is a fair test.

_____ and

_____ *(2 marks)*

Q5b

subtotal

c) He finds out that sandy soil has large particles but clay soil has much smaller particles.

Which type of soil – sandy or clay – will let the water pass through faster?

✎ _____

Explain your answer.

✎ _____

_____ *(1 mark)*

(Total 4 marks)

Using a Key

6   Class 6 visit a farm. They see these animals.

cow   fish   worm   duck

a) Tick **TWO** boxes that show the two animals that need water in their habitat.

✎ **cow** ☐   **fish** ☐   **worm** ☐   **duck** ☐   *(1 mark)* ☐

Q6a

Class 6 sort the animals using a key.

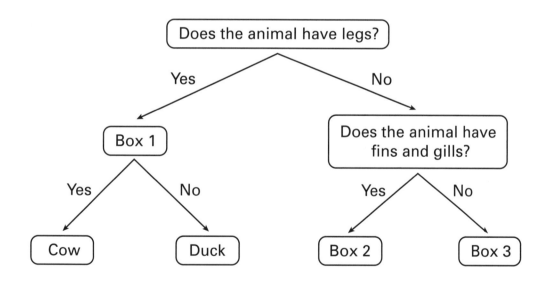

b) Tick **ONE** box to show what should be written in Box 1.

✎ **Does the animal have legs?**   ☐

   Does the animal have two legs?   ☐

   Does the animal have more than two legs?   ☐   *(1 mark)* ☐

Q6b

   subtotal

c) What should be written in Box 2? Circle the correct word.

✎   **cow**   **duck**   **fish**   **worm**   *(1 mark)*

d) What should be written in Box 3? Circle the correct word.

✎   **cow**   **duck**   **fish**   **worm**   *(1 mark)*

e) Tick **ONE** box to show the reason why we classify animals.

✎ **To group animals that live in water**   ☐

To help identify animals   ☐

To help draw a food chain   ☐   *(1 mark)*

(Total 5 marks)

Concert

7 Liam, Scott and Jason go to a rock concert. Liam stands near the stage. Scott and Jason are further back.

a) Who hears the loudest noise? Tick **ONE** box.

✎ **Jason** ☐   **Liam** ☐   **Scott** ☐   *(1 mark)* ☐

Q7a

b) Explain why he hears the loudest noise.

✎ _____ *(1 mark)* ☐

Q7b

c) The drummer hits the drum skin with his drumstick.

What happens to the drum skin when it makes a sound?

✎ _____ *(1 mark)* ☐

Q7c

subtotal

d) The drummer has different sizes of drums.

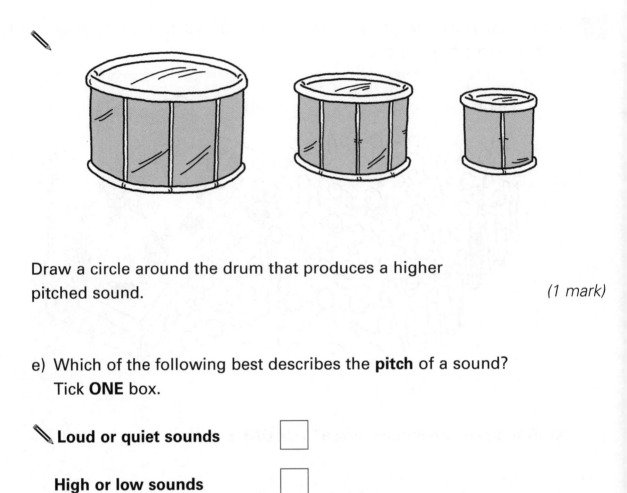

Draw a circle around the drum that produces a higher pitched sound.

(1 mark)

e) Which of the following best describes the **pitch** of a sound? Tick **ONE** box.

Loud or quiet sounds ☐

High or low sounds ☐

Long or short notes ☐

(1 mark)

(Total 5 marks)

Milk from Milk Powder

8 Instant milk powder is useful when fresh milk is not available.

a) How is instant milk powder made into liquid milk?

✎ _____

_____ *(1 mark)*

Q8a

b) i Instant milk powder is made by spraying skimmed milk onto heated rollers. The milk powder can be scraped off the rollers.

What change happens on the rollers?

✎ _____

_____ *(1 mark)*

Q8bi

ii Is the change that takes place on the rollers reversible or non-reversible? Explain your answer.

✎ _____

_____

_____ *(1 mark)*

Q8bii

(Total 3 marks)

END OF TEST

subtotal

Set

B

KEY STAGE 2
Levels 3–5

Test Paper 1

Science

Test Paper 1

Test Paper 1

Instructions:

- find a quiet place where you can sit down and complete the test paper undisturbed

- make sure you have all the necessary equipment to complete the test paper

- read the questions carefully

- answer all the questions in this test paper

- go through and check your answers when you have finished the test paper

✎ This pencil shows where you will have to put your answer. Sometimes you may have to draw the answer instead of writing one.

Time:

This test paper is **45 minutes** long.

Note to Parents:

Check how your child has done against the Answers and Mark Scheme on pages 315–316.

Page	227	229	231	233	235	237	239	241	Max. Mark	**Actual Mark**
Score	....	....	....	....	....	....	....	....	40	....

First name ....

Last name ....

Watering Plants

1 Adam and Becky are trying to find out if plants need water to grow and, if so, how much water they need to grow.

Adam has four plants. He adds different amounts of water to each plant every day.

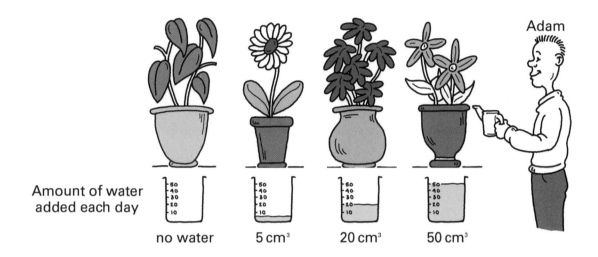

Amount of water
added each day

no water   5 cm³   20 cm³   50 cm³

Adam

Adam measures the height of the plants every week.

a) Why does Adam's teacher think this is not a fair test?

✎ _____

_____ *(1 mark)*

Becky has ten plants in each tray.

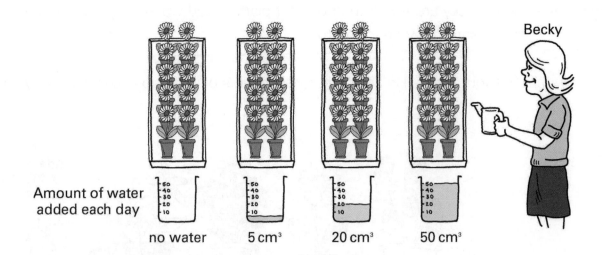

Amount of water
added each day

no water   5 cm³   20 cm³   50 cm³

Becky

b) Do you think Becky's experiment is a fair test?

i   Tick **ONE** box.   Yes [　]   No [　]

ii Give a reason for your answer.

_____

_____ (1 mark)

Here are their results.

Adam's results

Amount of water (cm³)	Height of plants (cm)			
	at start	week 1	week 2	week 3
0	10	dead	dead	dead
5	6	7		9
20	4	dead	dead	dead
50	6	6	dead	dead

Adam forgot to write down the height for 5 cm³ of water for week 2.

c) **Complete the table to show what the reading might have been.** *(1 mark)*

Q1c

Becky's results

Amount of water (cm³)	Average height of plants (cm)			
	at start	week 1	week 2	week 3
0	5	dead	dead	dead
5	5	6	7	8.5
20	5	8	10	11
50	5	5	dead	dead

subtotal

d) Becky starts to draw a line graph of the height of plants with 20 cm³ of water.

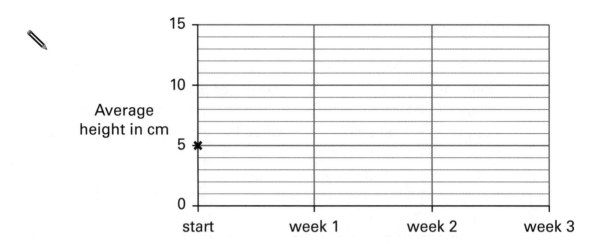

    i   **Finish plotting the points.**   *(2 marks)*
        The first one has been done for you.

    ii **Draw a line through the points.**   *(1 mark)*

e) Adam makes a conclusion for his results:

Becky says:

    i   **Who do you agree with? Tick ONE box.**

       Agree with Adam ☐   Agree with Becky ☐

ii Suggest why you agreed with either Adam or Becky.

_____

_____ *(1 mark)*

f) Write a conclusion for Becky's results.

_____

_____

_____ *(2 marks)*

(Total 9 marks)

Purifying Rock Salt

2 Jemima has some crushed rock salt. She looks at a sample with a hand lens.

    a) i **What will she see?**

    ✎ _____

        _____ *(1 mark)*

    ii **Why is this?**

    ✎ _____

        _____ *(1 mark)*

    She adds some of the rock salt to water and she stirs the mixture.

    b) Why does this separate the salt from the other impurities?

    ✎ _____

        _____ *(2 marks)*

c) i Draw a diagram showing how she could separate the mixture. *(1 mark)*

Label your diagram.

ii What is the name of this process?

_____ *(1 mark)*

d) Jemima wants to recover the pure salt.

i Put a ring around the best word to describe the method she uses. *(1 mark)*

burning   condensing   evaporating   melting

ii Draw a diagram showing how she could recover the salt.   (1 mark)

Label your diagram.

e) i   What would Jemima see if she looked at the salt she had recovered
        through a hand lens?

_____ (1 mark)

ii Why is this?

_____

_____ (1 mark)

(Total 10 marks)

Forces

3 Tim is measuring the force needed to pull his shoe across a wooden floor. He attaches a force meter to his shoe and pulls.

The reading on the force meter is 4**N**.

a) Tick **ONE** box to show what N stands for.

✎ **Newton** ☐   **Nitrogen** ☐   **Nought** ☐   *(1 mark)*   ☐

Q3a

b) Tim and Nick want to find out if different floor surfaces will affect the force needed to pull the shoe.

What is the ONE factor they should change as they carry out their investigation?

✎ _____*(1 mark)*   ☐

Q3b

c) Name **ONE** of the factors they should keep the same to make their investigation fair.

✎ _____*(1 mark)*   ☐

Q3c

subtotal

d) They carry out their investigation three times. Here are their results.

Force needed to pull the shoe

Floor surface	Force (N)		
	test 1	test 2	test 3
carpet	12	12	13
wood	9	4	10
vinyl	3	4	3

i   For which floor surface does one of the results seem unlikely?

_____ *(1 mark)*

ii   Which floor surface needed the most force to move the shoe?

_____ *(1 mark)*

e) The picture shows Tim pulling the shoe.

Label the arrows on the picture to say what **forces** they show.
One force has been labelled for you.

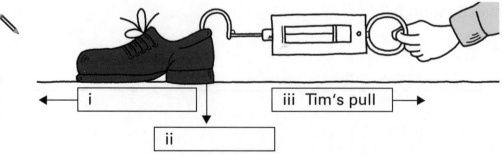

(2 marks)

(Total 7 marks)

Baking Bread

4 A baker is making bread. He mixes the ingredients including flour, water and yeast. He forms a dough. He leaves this in a warm place for a few hours.

a) i What happens to the dough when it is left?

_____ *(1 mark)*

ii Why is this important?

_____

_____ *(1 mark)*

b) i What is done to the dough to turn it into the final loaf of bread?

_____

_____ *(1 mark)*

ii How does the dough change during this process?

_____

_____ *(1 mark)*

(Total 4 marks)

The Dentist

5 Sally visits her dentist.

a) The dentist removes one of Sally's milk teeth. The dentist tells Sally there will not be a gap in her teeth for long.

   Why is this?

   ✎ _____

   _____ *(1 mark)*

b) The dentist tells Sally about the different types of teeth and the job they do.

   Draw THREE lines to match each type of tooth to the job it does.

   ✎ **Type of tooth**   **Job it does**

   | incisor | | tearing food |

   | canine | | cutting food |

   | molar | | chewing food | *(2 marks)*

c) The dentist tells Sally that some foods will damage her teeth.

Tick **TWO** boxes to show which foods will damage teeth.

apples ☐

carrots ☐

chocolates ☐

sweets ☐   *(2 marks)* ☐

(Total 5 marks)

subtotal

Sundials

6 Sundials have been used to find the time for hundreds of years.

a) How does a sundial use light from the Sun to show the time?

✏ _____

_____ *(2 marks)*

b) What is the time shown on this sundial?

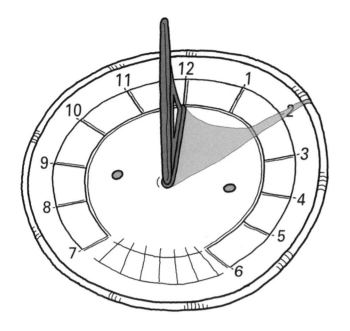

✎ _____ (1 mark)

c) At 12:00 noon in the summer, the Sun is ...

Tick **TWO** boxes.

✎ **due south.** ☐

due north. ☐

high in the sky. ☐

low in the sky. ☐ (2 marks)

(*Total 5 marks*)

END OF TEST

Set
B

KEY STAGE 2
Levels 3–5

Test Paper 2

Science

Test Paper 2

Test Paper 2

Instructions:

- find a quiet place where you can sit down and complete the test paper undisturbed

- make sure you have all the necessary equipment to complete the test paper

- read the questions carefully

- answer all the questions in this test paper

- go through and check your answers when you have finished the test paper

✎ This pencil shows where you will have to put your answer. Sometimes you may have to draw the answer instead of writing one.

Time:

This test paper is **45 minutes** long.

Note to Parents:

Check how your child has done against the Answers and Mark Scheme on page 317.

Page	243	245	247	249	251	253	255	256	Max. Mark	**Actual Mark**
Score	....	....	....	....	....	....	....	....	40	....

First name _____

Last name _____

Looking around the Kitchen

1 Jo collects a number of things from the kitchen.

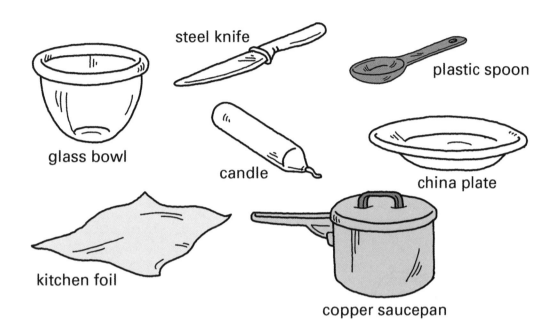

a) Which **THREE** things are made of metal?

✎ _____

_____

_____ *(2 marks)*

Q1a

b) Which thing is transparent?

✎ _____ *(1 mark)*

Q1b

subtotal

c) Why is copper a good material to use for making saucepans?

_____ (1 mark)

d) Which thing is attracted to a magnet?

_____ (1 mark)

e) Jo finds that the knife scratches the candle and the plastic spoon.
   The plastic spoon scratches the candle.

Put these three things in order of hardness. Put the softest one first.

softest   _____

               _____

hardest   _____   (2 marks)

(Total 7 marks)

The Heart

2 a) **On the diagram** mark the position of the heart with the letter **H**.

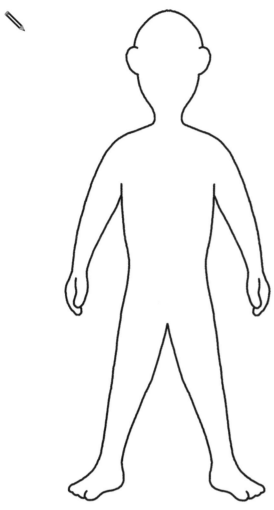

(1 mark) ☐
Q2a

b) Which part of the body protects the heart? Tick **ONE** box.

✎ **hair** ☐   **skin** ☐   **skull** ☐   **ribs** ☐   *(1 mark)* ☐
Q2b

c) Which blood vessels take blood away from the heart? Circle **ONE** word.

✎   **arteries**   **capillaries**   **veins**   *(1 mark)* ☐
Q2c

subtotal

d) Which blood vessels take blood to the heart? Circle **ONE** word.

arteries   **capillaries**   **veins**   (1 mark)

e) What is the job of the heart?

_____

_____ (2 marks)

(Total 6 marks)

Cooling Curves

3 Mrs Brown is showing Class 6 an experiment. She has a glass beaker containing very hot water. She puts a temperature probe into the water. She covers the beaker with a lid.

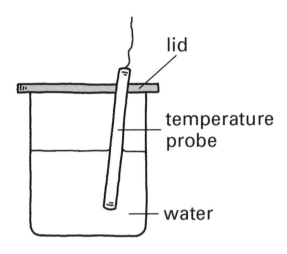

a) What could she use if she did not have a temperature probe?

_____ *(1 mark)*

Q3a

The computer takes the temperature of the water every 15 seconds and draws a graph of the results.

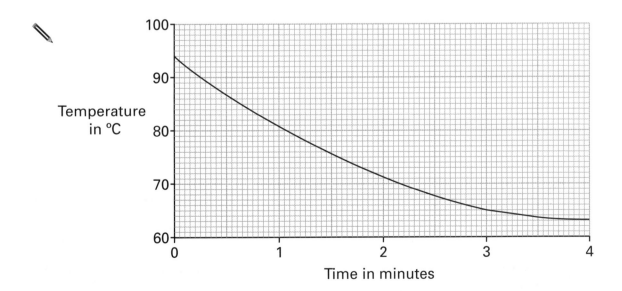

subtotal

b) What was the starting temperature of the water in the beaker?

✎ _____ (1 mark)

c) What was the temperature after 3 minutes?

✎ _____ (1 mark)

d) Sam says that the temperature may not be the same throughout the water.

What could Mrs Brown do to make sure it is?

✎ _____ (1 mark)

e) Mrs Brown does the experiment again, wrapping an insulator around the beaker.

On the grid on page 247, sketch the graph you would expect the computer to show. (2 marks)

f) The class are then set a problem:

'How would they find out whether felt is an insulator?'

They keep the beaker the same.

Write down TWO other things they should keep the same.

✎ _____

_____ (2 marks)

(Total 8 marks)

Motors

4 Kerry makes this circuit. The motor is turning a fan.

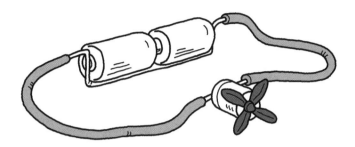

a) Describe how the motor is turning the fan in each of the circuits below. Choose words from this list. You can use them once, more than once or not at all.

not turning   **turning fast**   **turning slowly**

The first one has been done for you.   *(3 marks)*

Q4a

A

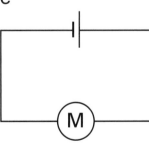

not turning

B

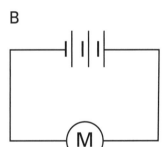

C

D

subtotal

b) Why is the motor not turning in Circuit A?

_____

_____ *(1 mark)*

(Total 4 marks)

Making Bread

5   Tom's class are going to make bread. Mr Smith shows them what to do.
The pictures show how he makes the bread.

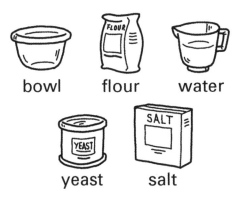

1 Collect ingredients

2 Mix together

3 Leave in a warm place

4 Ready to be baked

a) Before they start, all the children have to wash their hands.

    Why is this?

_____

_____ *(1 mark)*

Q5a

subtotal

b) Tom makes his bread. He forgets to leave it in a warm place.

Tick **ONE** box to show the effect this will have on his bread.

His bread will rise faster. ☐

His bread will rise very slowly. ☐

His bread will not rise at all. ☐

There will be no effect on his bread. ☐ *(1 mark)*

c) Why does sugar need to be added to the mixture?

_____

_____ *(1 mark)*

d) Jane makes her bread. She forgets to add the yeast.

Describe how Jane's bread will look by stage 4 on page 251.

_____

_____ *(1 mark)*

e) Yeast is a microbe.

Tick **TWO** boxes to show which foods are made by using microbes.

cheese ☐

chocolate ☐

meat ☐

potatoes ☐

yoghurt ☐   *(2 marks)* ☐

(Total 6 marks)

subtotal

Bike Ride

6 Rachael rides her bike early in the morning on a long journey.
The Sun is low in the sky.

a) Rachael can see a puddle on the road.

On the diagram draw a line to show how Rachael can see the puddle.
Label your line with a **P.**
(2 marks)

b) During her bike ride, the position of the Sun in the sky changes.

Draw a line on the same diagram that shows the movement of the Sun
during the day. Label the line **S.** Mark the position of the Sun at midday.
(2 marks)

(Total 4 marks)

Birthday Party

7 It is Steven's birthday. Steven looks at the candles on his birthday cake.

a) The candles give out light.

Circle **TWO** other objects that give out light.

✎ **lit torch bulb** **Moon** **satellite** **Sun** *(1 mark)* ☐

Q7a

b) Steven's friends sing 'Happy Birthday'.

Steven's mum walks away from the children and leaves the room.

What happens to the sound Steven's mum hears as she goes further away from the children?

✎ _____ *(1 mark)* ☐

Q7b

subtotal

c) Steven's mum shuts the wooden door. She can still hear the children singing. One material the sound is travelling through is air.

   Name ONE other material the sound is travelling through for Steven's mum to hear it.

   _____ *(1 mark)*

d) Steven is holding a balloon. The balloon is filled with helium.

   What TWO things are pulling the balloon down?

   _____

   _____ *(2 marks)*

(Total 5 marks)

END OF TEST

Set
C

KEY STAGE 2
Levels 3–5

Test Paper 1

Science

Test Paper 1

Test Paper 1

Instructions:

- find a quiet place where you can sit down and complete the test paper undisturbed
- make sure you have all the necessary equipment to complete the test paper
- read the questions carefully
- answer all the questions in this test paper
- go through and check your answers when you have finished the test paper

✎ This pencil shows where you will have to put your answer. Sometimes you may have to draw the answer instead of writing one.

Time:

This test paper is **45 minutes** long.

Note to Parents:

Check how your child has done against the Answers and Mark Scheme on pages 318–319.

Page	259	261	263	265	267	269	271	272	Max. Mark	**Actual Mark**
Score	....	....	....	....	....	....	....	....	40	....

First name

Last name

Football

1 Alex is practising his football skills. He is kicking the ball into the goal.

a) Which diagram shows the force acting on the ball as it hits the net?

Draw a circle around the correct diagram.

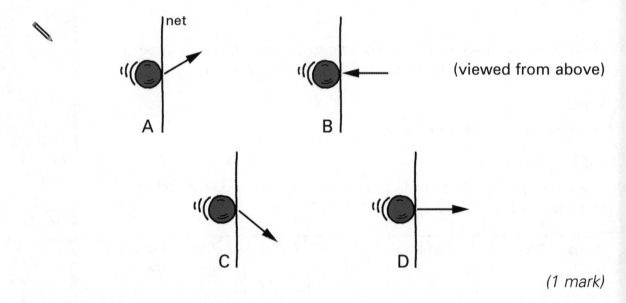

(viewed from above)

(1 mark)

b) Tick **TWO** boxes that show **two** things that change when the ball bounces off the net.

The colour of the net ☐   The shape of the net ☐

The colour of the ball ☐   The direction of the ball ☐   *(2 marks)*

Alex kicks the ball across the football pitch. The ball does not travel very far.

Next time, Alex kicks the ball very hard.

c) **What happens to the distance the ball travels on this second kick, compared to the first kick?**

_____

_____ *(1 mark)*

Q1c

subtotal

Alex kicks the ball up into the air.

d) What force makes the ball return to the ground?

_____ (1 mark)

(Total 5 marks)

Reaction with a Fizz

2 Class 6 watch an experiment. Mr Smith drops a spoonful of liver salts into a
beaker of cold water and stirs the solution.

They see the mixture fizz and a colourless gas escapes from the beaker.
Then he drops a spoonful of salt into another beaker of cold water and stirs
the solution. Mr Smith tells them that the change with liver salts is **not**
reversible but the change with salt is **reversible**.

a) **Can they get the liver salts and the salt back from the final solutions?**

✎ liver salts _____

   salt _____ *(1 mark)* ☐

   Q2a

b) **Which of the following suggests that the change with liver salts is not
   reversible? Tick ONE box.**

✎ **Mr Smith stirs the mixture.** ☐   **The mixture fizzes.** ☐

   The solution left is colourless. ☐   **The change is quick.** ☐ *(1 mark)* ☐

   Q2b

subtotal

c) Mr Smith does the experiment again. This time he weighs the beaker of water and the solid before, and the solution afterwards.

    i How would you expect the mass to change when liver salts are added to water?

✎ _____ *(1 mark)*

       Why is this?

✎ _____

_____ *(1 mark)*

   ii How would you expect the mass to change when salt is added to water?

✎ _____ *(1 mark)*

       Why is this?

✎ _____

_____ *(1 mark)*

d) Why is it important that liver salts are sold in a tin with a tight lid, rather than in a cardboard box?

_____

_____ (1 mark)

Q2d

(Total 7 marks)

subtotal

Bones and Muscles

3 Ben and Sarah are learning about bones.

a) Write a label in each box. Use words from this list.

ribs   **skull**   **spine**

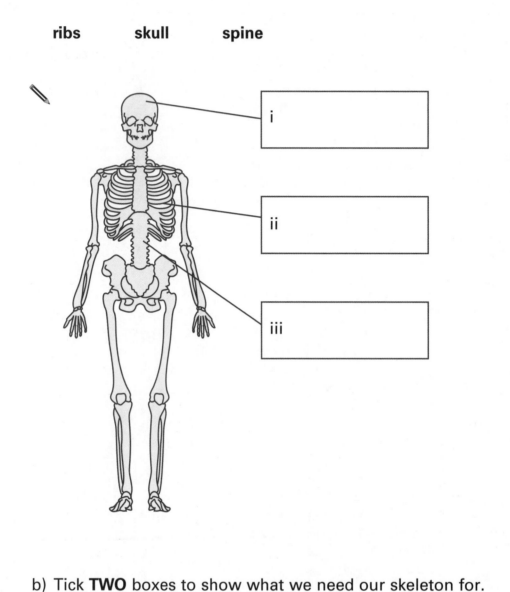

i

ii

iii

(2 marks)

b) Tick **TWO** boxes to show what we need our skeleton for.

To keep us warm ☐   **To help us move** ☐

To support our body ☐   **To help us think** ☐   *(2 marks)*

c) Ben has some ideas about his skeleton.

Write **true** or **false** below each idea.

(3 marks)

d) Ben is playing football. Sarah is sitting down watching him. Ben says his muscles are tired. Sarah says her muscles are not tired.

Why are Ben's muscles tired?

_____

_____ *(1 mark)*

(Total 8 marks)

subtotal

Mirrors

4 Class 5B are investigating mirrors. Jane uses her mirror to look at a spot on her chin.

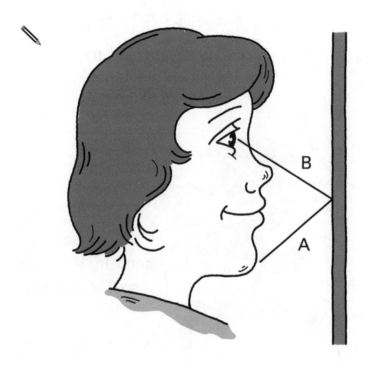

a) **On the diagram** draw one arrowhead on each of the lines
   A and **B** to show how the light travels. *(2 marks)*

b) Which word describes what happens to the light at the mirror?
   Circle your choice.

   deflection   **inflection**   **reflection**   **refraction**   *(1 mark)*

c) Jane and Laura are looking into a mirror, but there is a book between them.

Jane shines a torch onto the mirror so that Laura can see the torch.

Jane   Laura

On the diagram draw lines to show how Laura can see the torch. *(2 marks)*

Q4c

d) Jane uses a piece of paper instead of the mirror.

Why can Laura not see the torch?

_____

_____ *(1 mark)*

Q4d

(Total 6 marks)

subtotal

Earth, Sun and Moon

5 Mrs Smiles shows Class 5C a model of the Earth, Sun and Moon.
She uses a lamp for the Sun and a football for the Earth.

Sun

Earth

a) **On the diagram** shade the part of the Earth that is in darkness. *(1 mark)*

b) Mrs Smiles wants to show the class how day becomes night.

What should Mrs Smiles do to show this?

Write below or draw on the diagram.

_____ *(1 mark)*

c) Mrs Smiles wants to show the class the position of the Moon.

What could she use for the Moon?

_____ *(1 mark)*

d) **On the diagram** on page 268 draw the Moon in its
correct position. *(1 mark)*

(Total 4 marks)

Life Cycle of a Plant

6 The picture shows a growing plant.

The diagram shows the life cycle of a flowering plant.

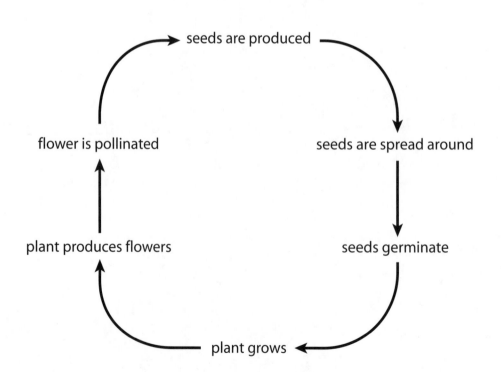

a) Tick the **TWO** boxes that show how seeds can be spread around. *(2 marks)*

✎ **animals** ☐   **crawl** ☐   **walk** ☐   **wind** ☐

b) What happens when seeds germinate?

✎ _____

_____ *(1 mark)*

c) Tick **TWO** boxes to show **two** conditions needed for germination. *(2 marks)*

✎ **gravity** ☐   **light** ☐   **moisture** ☐   **warmth** ☐   **wind** ☐

d) Which stage of the life cycle is often carried out by insects?

✎ _____ *(1 mark)*

(Total 6 marks)

Water Cycle

7 The diagram shows the water cycle.

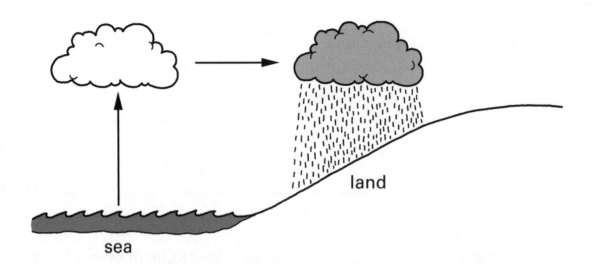

sea

land

Finish the explanation of the water cycle. Use words from this list in your answer.

boils   clouds   condenses   evaporates   freezes   vapour

✎ Water falls from the skies as rain when the clouds cool and the water vapour

_____. The rain water runs into streams and

finally into the sea. The water in the sea _____

to form water _____. This produces

_____ and the cycle continues.

(Total 4 marks)

END OF TEST

Test Paper 2

Instructions:

- find a quiet place where you can sit down and complete the test paper undisturbed
- make sure you have all the necessary equipment to complete the test paper
- read the questions carefully
- answer all the questions in this test paper
- go through and check your answers when you have finished the test paper

 This pencil shows where you will have to put your answer. Sometimes you may have to draw the answer instead of writing one.

Time:

This test paper is **45 minutes** long.

Note to Parents:

Check how your child has done against the Answers and Mark Scheme on pages 319–320.

Page	275	277	279	281	283	285	286	Max. Mark	**Actual Mark**
Score	....	....	....	....	....	....	....	40	....

First name ....

Last name ....

A Walk in the Country

1 Lee goes for a walk in the country.

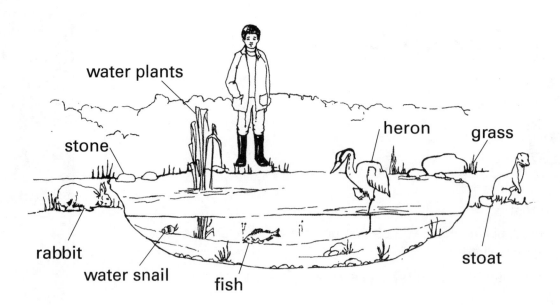

a) Lee can see different animals living in different habitats.

Finish the table by writing the name of an animal that lives in the habitat.

Habitat	Animal
pond	
field	

(2 marks)

b) Finish the table by writing the name of **ONE** living thing and **ONE** non-living thing.

Living thing	Non-living thing

(1 mark)

c) Write down **TWO** things that living things can do which non-living things cannot do.

✎ _____

_____ *(2 marks)*

d) Lee can see the water snails eating the water plants. He knows that fish eat water snails.

Finish the food chain. The last part has been done for you.

✎ [　　　] → [　　　] → [　　　] → [heron]

(1 mark)

e) Finish the table by writing the name of **ONE** thing in each column.

Producer	Prey	Predator

(3 marks)

(Total 9 marks)

Our Solar System

2 The Sun, the Earth and the Moon are three objects in our Solar System.

a) Which object is the same shape as the Earth? Tick **ONE** box.

A 2p coin ☐

A football ☐

A 50p coin ☐

A breakfast cereal box ☐ *(1 mark)*

b) Adam has some ideas about the Sun, Earth and Moon.

Write **true** or **false** below each idea.

1 The Sun and the Moon both go around the Earth.

_____

2 The Earth and the Moon both go around the Sun.

_____

3 It takes one year for the Earth to orbit the Sun.

_____

(2 marks)

The picture shows the position of the Sun early in the morning in summer.

c) **On the diagram** draw the position of the Sun at midday. Label this with an **M**.

(1 mark)

Q2c

d) **On the diagram** draw the position of the Sun in the evening, before sunset. Label this with an **E**.

(1 mark)

Q2d

(Total 5 marks)

subtotal

Melting Ice

3 Kim takes a glass out of the refrigerator. It has been in there some time. It contains cubes of ice floating in water.

ice

water

a) The ice cubes float in water.

What does that tell you about ice?

_____ *(1 mark)*

b) Kim measures the temperature of the mixture of ice and water.

i **Write down the name of the piece of apparatus she uses.**

_____ *(1 mark)*

ii **Draw a ring around the likely temperature of ice and water.**

−10°C   **0°C**   **10°C**   **20°C**   *(1 mark)*

c) She leaves the glass on the work surface until the ice has just turned to water.

   i Is ice turning to water a reversible or a non-reversible change? Explain your answer.

✎ _____

_____ *(1 mark)*

   ii What name is given to the change from ice to water?

✎ _____ *(1 mark)*

Q3cii

   iii The outside of the glass standing on the work surface goes misty. Why is this?

✎ _____

_____ *(2 marks)*

Q3ciii

d) Kim takes another glass containing ice and water out of the refrigerator. She adds salt to the mixture.

What happens to the temperature of the mixture?

✎ _____ *(1 mark)*

Q3d

(Total 8 marks)

subtotal

Cress Seeds

4 Emily and Lucy are growing cress plants. They put them in three different places.

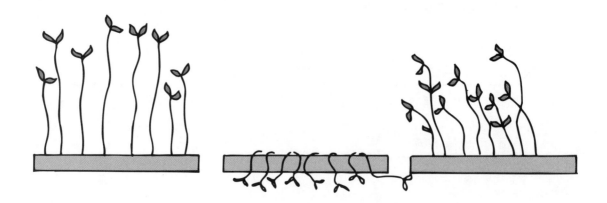

in a greenhouse   in a dark, warm cupboard   on a windowsill

a) Emily says this was not a fair test because they forgot to water the plants in the cupboard.

Tick **TWO** boxes to show two other things that made this an unfair test.

They were left for the same length of time.

It was warmer in the greenhouse.

Different cress seeds were used to grow the plants.

The same containers were used.

The seeds were planted in the same type of soil.   *(2 marks)*

b) Lucy makes lots of conclusions for this experiment.

For each of Lucy's conclusions tick **ONE** box.

	True	False	Can't tell
The plants in the cupboard died because they had no light.	☐	☐	☐
The plants on the windowsill grew towards the light.	☐	☐	☐
Warmth is needed for plants to grow.	☐	☐	☐
The plants in the greenhouse died.	☐	☐	☐

(4 marks)

Q4b

c) Finish the sentence. Choose your word from this list.

flowers   **leaves**   **roots**   **stems**

Plants take in water through their _____ *(1 mark)*

Q4c

(Total 7 marks)

subtotal

Types of Sugar

5 Granulated sugar, caster sugar and icing sugar are three types of sugar you might have in your kitchen. Granulated sugar has larger crystals than caster sugar. Icing sugar is a fine powder.

Tony adds one tablespoonful of granulated sugar to 100 cm³ of water and stirs it until he can no longer see the sugar. He repeats the experiment twice more.

Then he carries out the whole experiment using icing sugar and caster sugar.

His results are shown in the table.

Type of sugar	Time for sugar to disappear in seconds		
	1st experiment	2nd experiment	3rd experiment
granulated	45	50	52
icing	20	12	22
caster	32	34	35

a) Which word best describes what happens when sugar is added to water and it can no longer be seen?

Put a ring around the best word.

dissolve   **evaporate**   **melt**   *(1 mark)*

b) Why did Tony test each sugar three times?

_____

_____ *(1 mark)*

c) Tony looks at his results and thinks that one result is wrong.

Which result is wrong?

✎ _____ *(1 mark)*

d) How does the size of the sugar grains affect the time for the sugar to dissolve?

✎ _____

_____ *(2 marks)*

e) Tony has used the same amount of sugar and the same amount of water each time.

Suggest one other thing that might affect the results.

✎ _____ *(1 mark)*

f) Suggest one other thing Tony could do to make granulated sugar dissolve faster.

✎ _____

_____ *(1 mark)*

(Total 7 marks)

Stretching Elastic Bands

6 Mohammed is experimenting with elastic bands and masses. He puts a mass onto the hanger and records the length of the elastic band. Mohammed adds more masses.

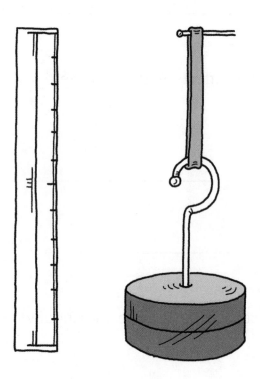

a) What could happen that makes this experiment unsafe?

_____

_____ (1 mark)

Mohammed drew a line graph of his results.

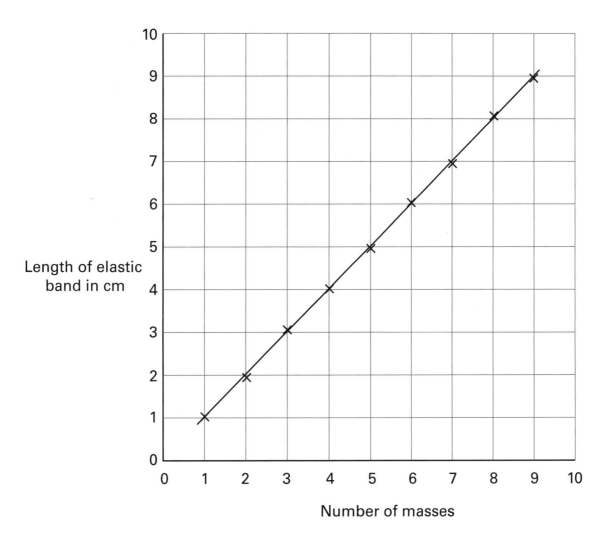

b) What is the length of the elastic band when four masses are added?

✎ _____ cm

(1 mark)

Q6b

c) Predict the length of the elastic band when ten masses are added.

✎ _____ cm

(1 mark)

Q6c

subtotal

d) Describe what Mohammed's graph tells him about the **number of masses** and **the length of the elastic band**.

_____

_____

_____ (1 mark)

(Total 4 marks)

END OF TEST